Human Resource Management in Aviation

Human Resource Management in Aviation

Proceedings of the XVIII WEAAP Conference:
Volume I

Edited by
Eric Farmer

Psychology Division

Royal Air Force Institute of Aviation Medicine

Farnborough, UK

Avebury Technical
Aldershot · Brookfield USA · Hong Kong · Singapore · Sydney

Published by
Avebury Technical
Academic Publishing Group
Gower House
Croft Road
Aldershot
Hants GU11 3HR
England

Gower Publishing Company
Old Post Road
Brookfield
Vermont 05036
USA

British Library Cataloguing in Publication Data
Human resource management in aviation: Proceedings of the XVIII WEAAP conference vol. I.
   1. Airlines. Personnel management
   I. Farmer, Eric II. Western European Association for Aviation Psychology
   387.70683

ISBN 1 85628 170 1

Printed in Great Britain by
Billing & Sons Ltd, Worcester

Contents

Simulation

Operational Issues

The Contributors

O Benn   Institute of Aviation, University of Illinois at Urbana-Champaign, Savoy, USA

S E Dale   Science 3 (Air), MoD, London, UK

D L Damos   University of Southern California, Los Angeles, USA

A Droog   Rijksluchtvaartschool, Paterwolde, The Netherlands

H J Dudfield   Flight Systems Department, Royal Aerospace Establishment, Farnborough, UK

H Eißfeldt   Department of Aviation and Space Psychology, German Aerospace Research Establishment (DLR), Hamburg, Germany

H Gordon   Scandinavian Institute of Aviation Psychology, Stockholm, Sweden

M Harsveld   Directorate of RNLAF, The Hague, The Netherlands

P G A M Jorna   TNO Institute for Perception, Soesterberg, The Netherlands

R H Kaiser   Institute of Aviation, University of Illinois at Urbana-Champaign, Savoy, USA

P Kline   Department of Psychology, University of Exeter, UK

J B Long   Ergonomics Unit, University College London, UK

A W MacRae   School of Psychology, University of Birmingham, UK

S E Pattison   School of Psychology, University of Birmingham, UK

S Phillips   Institute of Aviation, University of Illinois at Urbana-Champaign, Savoy, USA

J Rolfe	Science 3 (Air), MoD, London, UK
G Schuhfried	Hyrtlstraße 45, Mödling, Austria
S J Selcon	Psychology Division, RAF Institute of Aviation Medicine, Farnborough, UK
R A Shadrake	Psychology Division, RAF Institute of Aviation Medicine, Farnborough, UK
G Stead	Saville & Holdsworth Pty. Ltd., Balmain, Australia
A F Stokes	Aviation Research Laboratory, Institute of Aviation, University of Illinois, Willard Airport, Savoy, USA
P G C Tapsfield	Science 3 (Air), MoD, London, UK
H L Taylor	Institute of Aviation, University of Illinois at Urbana-Champaign, Savoy, USA
R M Taylor	Psychology Division, RAF Institute of Aviation Medicine, Farnborough, UK
R T B Visser	TNO Institute for Perception, Soesterberg, The Netherlands
J M Wilbourn	USAF Military Training Center, Lackland AFB, USA
R A Weinberg	Institute of Aviation, University of Illinois at Urbana-Champaign, Savoy, USA

Preface

Efficient management of human resources is particularly important in the aviation community. The chapters in this volume describe the efforts of aviation psychologists to enhance the efficiency and safety of flight operations. Civil and military aircrew, air traffic controllers, and passengers all receive attention.

The contributions are based upon papers presented to the XVIII conference of the Western European Association for Aviation Psychology (WEAAP) in Brighton, UK. Since its inception in 1956 by a group of nine psychologists, WEAAP's membership has rapidly increased, and the association now plays a major role in the promotion of aviation psychology. The contents of this book and its companion volume, *Stress and Error in Aviation,* reflect the wide-ranging interest in WEAAP's activities: researchers not only from Europe but from the United States and Australia have contributed to these volumes.

A significant feature of the XVIII conference was the invitation extended to leading academics to provide an overview and analysis of the papers. Their comments help to identify future directions that aviation psychology research should take.

Naturally, personnel selection remains an important human resource issue in aviation, and is well represented here. The predictive value of biographical factors, personality, and information processing ability are carefully examined. Approaches range from validation of a complete selection package to examination of the usefulness of a single test, the controversial Defence Mechanism Test that is based on an attempt to integrate perceptual and psychoanalytic theories. The contributions on training are similarly wide-ranging, including both guidelines for organizational development and use of a laboratory task to develop a training paradigm for situational awareness.

Other contributions illustrate the value of simulation both as a training aid and as a tool for the evaluation of new technology. Evidence is presented that even a low-cost computer game may permit investigation of the impact of new operational procedures.

The final section of the volume demonstrates the wide range of operational issues addressed by aviation psychologists. Cognitive theory is applied to the problem of identifying the most appropriate method of providing feedback to users of direct voice input systems; three types of training programme are compared; and the implications of a smoking ban for passenger comfort and safety are investigated. The volume concludes with a conceptualization that relates these and other issues and that can be seen as a first step toward an integrated framework for the discipline of aviation psychology.

Eric W. Farmer

Part I

Selection & Training

1

A validation study of the QANTAS pilot selection process
Greg Stead

ABSTRACT

Since 1960, Qantas Airways has used psychological testing and interviews to select pilots. Qantas began its current pilot recruitment programme in late 1983, and since then a number of changes have been made to various components of the selection process. A Flight Check and check in a B747 simulator were introduced in 1983 to add more skills evaluation to the selection process. In January 1986, a new range of ability, critical reasoning, and personality tests replaced the older tests, and in May 1987 a co-ordinator/skills tester, the Pilot Aptitude and Skills Tester (PAT), was purchased from the UK Ministry of Defence to permit further evaluation of skill and aptitude.

Qantas commissioned a validation study of the relationship between all the processes involved in the selection of pilots and the subsequent ground training, simulator training, and flight training reports on those who commenced employment with the airline from January 1986. Although emphasis was placed on the 'new' psychological assessment tests and the PAT results, the Flight and Simulator Checks were also fully evaluated.

This validation study is the most comprehensive of its type undertaken in commercial aviation in Australia and the results confirm the overall predictive efficiency of the current pilot selection process, with the possible exception of the Flight Check. The results also confirm the value of the psychological testing process and indicate how psychological test data can be integrated with the other predictors to achieve the optimum selection of commercial airline pilots.

INTRODUCTION

Psychological testing of pilot applicants has been an integral part of the pilot selection process at Qantas Airways since February 1960, and, although a number of earlier validation studies have been undertaken, none has involved the complexity or objectivity attempted in the present study.

3

This validation exercise sets out to study the relationship between all the processes involved in the selection of pilots for Qantas Airways Ltd. and the subsequent ground training, simulator training, and flight training reports on those applicants who commenced employment with the airline. A further aim was to investigate the relationships between failures in the simulator phase of training and selection performance.

The study covers only those pilots who commenced from January 1986, and, in the main, undertook a battery of psychological tests produced by Saville and Holdsworth Ltd. (SHL) and introduced into the pilot selection process in January 1986 to replace other tests used since 1960. In addition to the psychological test data, age, background (e.g. general aviation or military), flying hours, skills, and simulator and flight checks were investigated in this validation study. A total of 46 selection variables were measured, 37 from the psychological test battery alone (Appendix 1).

The selection process
All applicants who have met the minimum criteria enter stage A of the selection procedure. This stage involves:

 – psychological assessment testing
 – co-ordination/aptitude testing (PAT/Skills tester)
 – initial interview
 – eyesight medical

Those applicants considered suitable at this stage are then invited to attend stage B of the selection procedure. This stage involves:

 – a flight check in a light twin-engined aircraft (military pilots exempt)
 – a simulator check in a modified B747 simulator
 – a medical examination
 – a final interview

Successful applicants commence as pilots under initial training and all undertake the following ground and flight training programme before being checked out as Second Officers:

 – Initial Course
 – Type Course (B747 or B767)
 – Cockpit Procedures Trainer/Fixed Base Simulator (FBS)
 – Simulator
 – Flight Training

Appendices 2(a) to 2(e) present a brief description of the PAT (Skills tester), Simulator Check, Flight Check, Abilities and Critical Reasoning and the Personality components of the selection process. Appendix 3 provides means and standard deviations (SDs) for age and flying hours, and for PAT, Simulator and Flight Check results.

METHOD

Two hundred and thirty-four pilots who commenced employment with Qantas after January 1 1986 were included in this study. Of these, 199 had undertaken, during stage A of the selection process, the ability and verbal critical reasoning tests and the two Occupational Personality Questionnaires (OPQ). One hundred and ninety had completed the full range of assessments, including the numerical critical reasoning test added to the test battery at the beginning of February 1986.

All elements of the selection process (see Appendix 1) were investigated and the pilots were assessed against their performance on the Initial Course, Type Course, Fixed Based Simulator, and Simulator, and against Flight Training Reports (FT9s).

Performance criteria
The performance measures are described below. For each, a summary of course results is provided in Appendix 3.

Initial Course. A course designed to bring all pilots under initial training up to a minimum standard of knowledge on topics including modern instrument systems and high-speed flight. A pass mark of 80 has been set, based on a multiple-choice, closed book examination.

Type Course. A B747 or B767 technical course with a multiple-choice open book exam that has an overall pass mark of 80 except for Emergency Procedures and Fuel Systems which require a mark of 100 (maximum score).

Cockpit Procedures Trainer/Fixed Based Simulator. This phase involves the operation of systems and procedures including instruments and engineering. Students are assessed against a Company standard with marks ranging from a minimum of 1 (poor) to a maximum of 4.

Simulator. This leads to the provision of a 2nd Class endorsement on B747 and B767 aircraft including a restricted Flight Engineer Licence on the B747. Assessments are made to Company standards with marks ranging from a minimum of 1 (poor) to a maximum of 4.

Flight Training Reports (FT9s). These reports relate to performance in either the aircraft or the simulator, and may include normal Second Officer duties, support duties, Licence renewal and cyclic training. The pilots are assessed on a scale of 1 to 4.

LIMITATIONS

An important limitation of this study is that it is influenced by a restriction of range. Only those pilots who have successfully completed the selection procedure and who subsequently commenced employment with the airline are included. Applicants who failed to be selected are not represented. At this stage, no statistical correction has been made for the restriction of range; consequently, the results are likely to underestimate the predictive capacity of the selection variables. As an illustration, consider the correlation of 0.25 obtained between one measure, VA3, and performance on the Initial Training Course. The range of scores of the pilots studied was narrower than that of the entire applicant group (SDs 6.05 and 7.5, respectively). A 'formula for correction' applied to these figures raised the correlation from 0.25 to 0.31, an increase of almost 25%, which enhances the results obtained considerably.

Another limitation of this study is that it focuses primarily on training course performance and, to a lesser extent, on performance as rated by the FT9 reports. At best, the FT9 ratings include Simulator support, Licence Renewal and some Flight Deck performance in the early part of a pilot's flying career (i.e. as a Second Officer). Obviously, longer-term performance and effectiveness in both First Officer and Command roles will be dependent upon many factors, including skill and aptitude, and personality characteristics that are more objectively and efficiently evaluated in a psychological assessment process with known validities. However, there is already good evidence that the OPQ accurately predicts a wide range of management/leadership competencies and it is likely that many of these will be important to operational pilot success.

There is a need to evaluate longer-term performance against selection variables, but this is not possible in the present study, given the limitations that have been imposed of evaluating those who have, in the main, undertaken a battery of psychological tests produced by SHL.

RESULTS

The results of the validation study are summarized in Table 1 and show only those selection variables that correlate with course and/or FT9 performance at $p < 0.05$ or better.

1. Initial Course
The analysis of the correlations between the selection process and the Initial Course shows that nine variables are predictive of course results, which ranged from a minimum of 69 (fail) to a maximum of 99.5. Thus, these variables correlate with those pilots under initial training who performed well on the course.

2. Type Course (B747 and B767 combined)

Thirteen selection variables correlate with course performance, scores on which range from 80 (pass) to 99. No participants failed or had to repeat sessions during this phase of training.

3. Cockpit Procedures Trainer/FBS

Twelve selection variables correlate with performance in the Fixed Base Simulator, with scores for this phase of training ranging between a minimum of 1 (fail) and a maximum of 3.5. Those who failed to reach the minimum required standards were given repeat sessions to achieve a pass standard.

4. Simulator

Sixteen variables are predictive of performance in the simulator where the scores ranged from a minimum of 1 (fail) to a maximum of 5. Those trainee pilots who had failures at this Simulator stage of training were given repeat sessions in order to achieve minimum acceptable standards. Three trainees failed to achieve a satisfactory minimum level of performance and resigned from the airline.

5. Failures in the Simulator phase of training

Of the 234 pilots included in this study, 186 had progressed as far as the Simulator phase of their training programme. Of these 186, 25 had at least one failure, with 12 pilots under initial training experiencing multiple failures, including one with six failures. Table 1 indicates the 18 selection variables that correlate with the probability of a pilot under initial training having failures during the Simulator phase of training.

6. Flight Training Reports (FT9s)

A total of 186 pilots are included in this phase of the study, and 12 selection variables correlate with performance, with average ratings for each pilot ranging from 2 (minimum satisfactory progress) to a maximum of 3.5. A number of pilots had ratings below 2 in cyclic training, licence renewal or when operating as a support pilot (Second Officer) in one or more of ten operational sequences. However, the FT9 ratings are averaged over a number of checks and no Second Officer in this study was rated below minimum satisfactory progress overall.

Table 1 summarizes the selection variables that correlate with course and/or Flight Training (FT9) report performance.

Table 1: Selection variables correlating with performance

Variable	Initial Course	Type Course	FBS	Simulator	Simulator Failures	FT9
Background						
Age	...	...	....	.283*	-.152	.197*
Flying Hours	...	...	...	...	-.130	...
GA/Military	...	-.210	-.232*	-.343*	.193*	-.378*
Skills/Aptitude						
PAT (Skills Total)	.292*	.311*	.204*	.279*	-.267*	.284*
INSB	.315*	.293*	...	.234	-.291*	.277
SMA	...	...	.241*	.226	...	...
CVT	...	...	...	...	...	.320*
Simulator Check	.138	.215*	.263*	.252*	-.207*	.350*
Abilities						
Verbal Concepts (VA1)	...	.210*	.151	.333*	-.152	...
Number Series (NA2)	...	.194*	...	.234*	...	...
Diagrammatic Reasoning (DT8)	...	.217*	.190	.337*	-.178	...
Abilities Total	.162	.260*	.217*	.385*	-.188*	...
Verbal Critical Reasoning (VA3)	.250*	.309*	...	.258*	...	.216*
Numerical Critical Reasoning (NA4)	.196*	.251*	.175	.350*	-.174	.216*
Personality						
Persuasive (R1)	...	...	...	...	.159	...
Controlling (R2)	...	...	...	...	.204	...
Independence (R3)	.160	...	...	-.183	.163	...
Outgoing (R4)	...	...	...	-.164	.191*	...
Socially Confident (R6)	...	...	...	...	.141	...
Democratic (R8)	...	-.192*	...	...	...	-.250*
Practical (T1)	...	...	...	-.204*	...	...
Data Rational (T2)	.186*	...	...	...	...	...
Artistic (T3)	...	...	-.176	...	...	-.169
Traditional (T5)	...	-.233*	...	...	...	...
Change-Oriented (T6)	.145	...	...	...	...	...
Innovative (T8)	...	...	...	...	.167	...
Detail-Conscious (T10)	...	...	.178	...	...	...
Conscientious (T11)	...	...	.182	...	...	...
Competitive (F8)	...	-.157	...	-.161	.237*	
Achieving (F9)	...	...	-.200*	...	.225*	-.180
Decisive (F10)	...	...	...	...	...	.169

Notes: 1) * denotes $p < 0.01$, otherwise $p < 0.05$; 2) Military background pilots tend to perform better and are less likely to have simulator failures.

'Best combination' of selection variables: Multiple regression

The second phase of the analysis of the correlation results was to obtain a 'best combination' of the selection variables for each of the four ground courses and for the FT9 consensus results, using multiple regression analysis to identify the combination of selection variables with the greatest ability to predict course performance.

Multiple correlation provides an index of how well attributes such as ability, aptitude, motivation, and personality combine to predict the outcome of training and, indeed, of early flying performance as measured by the FT9 reports. The advantage of the multiple regression technique is that it enables weights to be assigned to attributes according to their overall contribution to the prediction of success. For example, both intellectual ability and determination may be required for success, but intellectual ability may be twice as important as determination. With multiple regression, therefore, optimum weights are assigned to the variables, and using these and other data it is possible to develop specification equations by which candidates can be assessed in terms of their likely performance in training and on the job. The 'best combinations' of selection variables appear in Table 2.

The combination of variables that correlates strongly with Initial Course performance includes one selection variable from the personality factors (Emotional Control [F4]) which by itself did not correlate with performance. Of the six selection variables predictive of Type Course performance, two (Traditional [T5] and Competitive [T8]) correlate negatively with performance, i.e. those pilots under initial training who achieve good results on the course tend to have lower scores on these two variables. Achieving (F9) correlates negatively with performance on the CPT/FBS; Independence (R3) and Practical (T1) both correlate negatively with performance in the simulator; and Democratic (R8) and Achieving (F9) correlate negatively with the consensus performance rating from the FT9 reports.

DISCUSSION

This validation study demonstrates that combinations of selection variables correlate significantly with performance in the four ground training courses (Initial Course, Type Course, Fixed Base Simulator, and Simulator) and with an averaged rating of performance from the FT9s. In addition, it has been shown that 18 variables correlated with the probability of a pilot under initial training having one or more failures during the Simulator phase of the training programme.

Given that this study is based upon pilots who have been successful during the selection process and have been appointed to Qantas, the results are very encouraging and point to the value of most aspects of the overall selection procedure.

Of the 46 selection variables, the PAT (skills total), Simulator Check, and Numerical Critical Reasoning (NA4) test correlate with performance over all four phases of the ground training programme, including simulator failures,

Table 2. Best combination of variables for prediction
of performance measures

Measure	Multiple R	Variables
Initial Course	.532	INSB
		Simulator Check
		Verbal Critical Reasoning (VA3)
		Independence (R3)
		Data Rational (T2)
		Change-Oriented (T6)
		Emotional Control (F4)
Type Course	.447	INSB
		Simulator Check
		Diagrammatic Reasoning (DT8)
		Verbal Critical Reasoning (VA3)
		Traditional (T5) (-)
		Competitive (F8) (-)
CPT/FBS	.483	SMA
		Simulator Check
		Diagrammatic Reasoning (DT8)
		Conscientious (T11)
		Achieving (F9)(-)
Simulator	.558	INSB
		Simulator Check
		Verbal Concepts (VA1)
		Numerical Critical Reasoning (NA4)
		Independence (R3)(-)
		Practical (T1)(-)
FT9	.530	CVT
		Simulator Check
		Numerical Critical Reasoning (NA4)
		Democratic (R8)(-)
		Achieving (F9)(-)
		Decisive (F10)

and with the FT9 reports. In all, 26 selection variables (see Table 1) correlate with performance in at least one of the ground training courses, or with the FT9 reports. The INSB and Abilities Total variables correlate against performance in five of the six criterion measures studied.

From the psychological testing process, in addition to the Abilities Total already mentioned, Verbal Concepts (VA1), Diagrammatic Reasoning (DT8), and Verbal Critical Reasoning (VA3) correlate with performance on four of the six criterion measures, and the personality variables of Independence (R3), Competitive (F8), and Achieving (F9) correlate with performance on three measures.

The results of this study also highlight the differences in performance between pilots from general aviation and military backgrounds. In all instances in which a significant correlation occurred, those pilots with military backgrounds tended to perform better and were more likely to have fewer (if any) failures in the simulator phase of training. These results are not surprising, since all military pilots have previously been subjected to a rigorous selection screening programme which involves psychological and aptitude testing and an equally, if not more, rigorous training programme. Also, military pilots are likely to have operated in multi-crew environments or, at least, as part of a team in the case of fighter pilots. Pilots with a general aviation background, on the other hand, have not experienced the same rigorous selection and training programmes, and there appear to be wider ranges in their skills and aptitude, in their intellectual abilities, and in their problem solving capacities; there are also some differences in their personality style. In addition, general aviation pilots are more than likely to have operated only as single pilots, and tend to be younger and have fewer flying hours.

Although these differences between general aviation and military pilots may be of lesser influence on performance and potential Command effectiveness over the longer term (a topic worthy of evaluation), these differences are predictive of performance in the early stages of a pilot's career with Qantas.

Below is a summary of the six criterion measures studied, and the selection variables that correlate with performance on each.

Initial Course
The pilots under initial training who achieved better results in this course tended to gain a higher PAT (Skills) score, particularly in the INSB exercise, have a better simulator check result, and have higher abilities and both verbal and numerical critical reasoning capacity; they were also more independent, data rational (comfortable working with numerical and statistical data), and change-oriented.

Type Course

Those who achieved better results in this course tended to be from a military background, gain a higher PAT (Skills) score, especially in the INSB exercise, have a better simulator check result, and have strong overall abilities, including verbal and numerical critical reasoning ability; they were less democratic (i.e. less reliant upon others in decision-making areas), less traditional and conservative in their thinking style, and less competitive.

Cockpit Procedures Trainer/Fixed Based Simulator

Those pilots under initial training who performed better tended to be from a military background, have a high PAT (Skills) score, especially in the SMA exercise, have a better simulator check result, have stronger overall abilities with emphasis on verbal concepts and diagrammatic reasoning, and have higher numerical critical reasoning results; they were less artistic in thinking style, more detail-conscious and precise, more conscientious and persevering, and less individually achieving (risk-taking/ambitious).

Simulator

Those pilots under initial training who achieved better results in the Simulator phase of training tended to be older, from a military background, have higher PAT (Skills) scores, especially in the INSB and SMA exercises, have a better Simulator check result, and have stronger overall abilities, including both verbal and numerical critical reasoning abilities; they were less independent and outgoing (sociable and talkative in their relationships with others), less practical in terms of working with machinery or physical work, and less individually competitive.

Simulator failures

A total of 25 pilots under initial training had at least one failure during the simulator training phase, with 12 trainees having two or more failures. Those having multiple failures tended to be younger, have fewer flying hours, have a general aviation background, have lower PAT (Skills) scores, especially in the INSB exercise, have lower simulator check results, have lower overall abilities, especially in their verbal concepts and diagrammatic reasoning results, and have lower numerical critical reasoning ability; they were also more persuasive (argumentative/influencing), more controlling (directive), more independent, more outgoing (sociable/talkative), more socially confident, more innovative, and more individually competitive and achieving in their behaviour.

In summary, these individuals tended to be more self-assured, assertive, and independent, but have lower skills, aptitude and lower overall abilities and problem solving capacity. They were perhaps not sufficiently aware of their weaknesses or potential failings as well as not having the overall skill and capacity to achieve consistently satisfactory results.

Flight Training Reports (FT9s)

From the FT9 reports, those who had a better averaged rating tended to be older, have a military background, have better PAT (Skills) results, especially in the INSB and CVT exercises, have better Simulator Checks, and have high verbal and numerical critical reasoning abilities; they were less democratic in their relationships with others, less artistic in their thinking style, less individually achieving and ambitious, and more decisive in their approach to their work.

An overall evaluation of the courses and FT9 reports shows that it is a combination of selection variables which tends to correlate with better performance. Skills (PAT), aptitude (Simulator), abilities, and/or critical reasoning capacity and a number of personality factors can be combined to predict better performance during the training phases and in general flying duties, simulator support, cyclic training, and licence renewal sessions that are typically covered by the FT9 reports.

Of the 46 selection variables assessed against course and FT9 performance, only the Flight Check, in the skills and aptitude area, failed to be a predictor of performance. This may, in part, be explained by the restricted range of results achieved by the 189 pilots who undertook the Flight Check exercise. The range of results was between 3 (recommended with reservations) to 5 (highly recommended). In comparison, the Simulator Check ranged between 2 (borderline) and 5, and was a good predictor of all course and FT9 performance. Another possible reason is that the Flight Check variable is unlikely to predict performance adequately when the applicant's PAT (Skills) score, simulator check result, and various psychological assessment components all show good results. This could be clarified only by fully evaluating a sample of pilot applicants who were unsuccessful in gaining employment with Qantas.

A number of the personality variables that correlate with performance deserve further comment:

Independence (R3). Although this variable correlated positively with performance in the Initial Course, it correlated negatively with performance in the simulator. This may well be due to the fact that pilots under initial training and in a new learning environment must work well as a part of a team to achieve a good result. Interestingly, those showing more independence in behaviour and who had simulator failures were more likely to have multiple failures during their simulator training exercises.

Democratic (R8). Individuals high on democracy tend to be consensus decision makers, involving everyone around them and taking some time to come to a decision. In this study, those pilots lower on the democratic variable tended to perform better on the Type Course and had better performance as rated by the FT9s. These pilots, though willing to listen to the opinions of others, are prepared to make their decisions even without consensus. This does not mean that they make hasty or rash decisions.

Competitive (F8) and Achieving (F9). Both these variables, although they appear (on the surface) to indicate determination, strong achievement-orientation, and ambition, tend to focus on quick, individual results, where rapid promotion and an element of risk-taking are evident. However, the pilots under initial training who performed better appeared more self-restraining, more willing to do well, but not independently of others, and more aware of the constraints, time and effort involved in achieving their ambitions.

Overall, those pilot applicants who have the skill and aptitude, combined with good abilities and critical reasoning capability as well as a balanced personality style, are more likely to achieve better course results and better FT9 reports. The results of this study highlight the fact that it is a combination of selection variables, not just one or two, that correlates with good performance. A comprehensive selection programme increases the likelihood of selecting pilots who will achieve good results.

The components of the selection process, with the possible exception of the Flight Check, form a comprehensive selection system that is capable of discriminating between the poorer and better performers; at least during the ground course stage and in the early stages of Second Officer flying, as indicated by the FT9 reports.

In analysing the results of this validation study, it is evident that the PAT (Skills tester), the Simulator, and the psychological tests of ability and personality are components of the selection process that lead to outcomes correlating with ground training and FT9 rating performance. The three ability and two critical reasoning tests and the two Occupational Personality Questionnaires included in the battery prove, either individually or in combination, to be significant predictors of performance in training and as assessed from the FT9 reports.

In overall terms, the psychological testing process is cost-effective when compared to other elements in the selection process, such as the Flight and Simulator Checks, and indeed, the interviews. However, the overall value of the psychological assessment process is that it is an independent and objective way of evaluating the suitability of an applicant, both over the short and longer terms, as a pilot with Qantas. The results are very encouraging and demonstrate the value of the psychological testing process and how the process can best be integrated with other predictive selection variables to achieve long-term efficiency in pilot selection.

Similarly, the PAT (total score) has proved to be a strong predictor of course and FT9 performance, with the INSB component being the most predictive of the three individual components of the PAT. The predictive capability, based on the results of this study, appears to confirm the suitability of the PAT to evaluate the aptitude of applicants who have flying experience.

As a side issue to this study, flying hours do not correlate with the PAT score or any of its three components. Moreover, there is no correlation between the PAT and the Flight Check, but there is a correlation between the total PAT score, the INSB, and the CVT with performance at the Simulator Check phase of the selection process. The Simulator Check results correlate well with all course and FT9 performance results and, like the PAT, do not correlate with Flying Hours or with the Flight Check.

These results indicate that the assessment of skills and aptitude and the capacity to predict training performance and future success as a pilot are more efficiently measured by the PAT and the Simulator rather than the Flight Check. However, as previously mentioned, the Flight Check requires further evaluation.

APPENDIX 1. MEASURES USED IN THE VALIDATION STUDY

Experience/background
Age; Flying Hours; General aviation/military background

Skills/aptitude
Pilot Aptitude and Skills Tester (PAT) comprising INSB, Sensory Motor Apparatus (SMA) and Control Velocity Test (CVT); Simulator Check (Modified B747 simulator); Flight Check (light twin-engined aircraft)

Abilities
Verbal Concepts (VA1); Numerical Series (NA2); Diagrammatic Reasoning (DT8); Abilities Total; Verbal Critical Reasoning (VA3); Numerical Critical Reasoning (NA4)

Personality
Persuasive (R1); Controlling (R2); Independence (R3); Outgoing/Sociability (R4); Affiliative (R5); Socially Confident (R6); Modest (R7); Democratic (R8); Caring (R9); Practical (T1); Data Rational (T2); Artistic (T3); Behavioural (T4); Traditional (T5); Change-Oriented (T6); Conceptual (T7); Innovative (T8); Forward Planning (T9); Detail-Conscious (T10); Conscientious (T11); Relaxed (F1); Worrying (F2); Tough-Minded (F3); Emotional Control (F4); Optimistic (F5); Critical (F6); Active (F7); Competitive (F8); Achieving (F9); Decisive (F10); Social Desirability (D1)

Ground training
Initial Course Results; Type Course Results; Fixed Based Simulator (FBS); Simulator ; Simulator Failures

Other
Flight Training Reports (FT9s)

APPENDIX 2. FURTHER INFORMATION ON MEASURES

(a) Pilot Aptitude and Skills Tester (PAT)

The PAT is a personal-computer-based system and is operated by a small keyboard, joystick control and foot controls (rudder pedals). The system is easy to use, even by those who are not computer-oriented, and presents the following tests:

Sensory Motor Apparatus (SMA). A psychomotor co-ordination test of eye, hand and foot co-ordination.

Control of Velocity Test (CVT). A psychomotor co-ordination test measuring eye-hand co-ordination.

Instrument Interpretation (INSB). A situation awareness test giving a measure of powers of observation, clear thinking and learning ability.

(b) Simulator Check

The Simulator Check is given to all Stage B candidates in a B747 simulator, modified to show a basic instrument panel so that candidates are not subjected to an unnecessary clutter of background instruments. The simulator is operated as a twin-engined aircraft which provides a good indication of scan-rate in an environment which more closely matches the candidate's experience. The one hour session assesses: basic instrument scan; co-ordination; straight and level flying skills; climbing and descending turns; steep turns; ILS interception and approach; ADF tracking, back-tracking, holding and approach.

(c) Flight Check

The Flight Check, given only to General Aviation pilots and lasting one hour, assesses: instrument flying technique (including ADF procedures); asymmetric flying technique; general flying skills and airmanship.

(d) Abilities and critical reasoning

The testing requires an applicant to undertake the five timed tests described below.

Verbal Concepts (15 minutes). This test measures advanced general verbal skills.

Numerical Series (15 minutes). This test is designed to measure higher order numerical reasoning ability.

Diagrammatic Reasoning (15 minutes). This test measures general reasoning skills which are based on logical and flexible thinking.

Verbal Critical Reasoning (30 minutes). This test is designed to measure the ability to evaluate critically and logically various types of argument. To achieve an answer, the individual must comprehend statements, select pertinent information from them, recognise the assumptions on which the statements are based, and evaluate this information.

Numerical Critical Reasoning (35 minutes). This test is designed to measure the ability to make correct decisions or inferences from numerical or statistical data. Although clearly related to various numerical aptitudes, this is a skills test intended to measure the candidate's ability to cope with figures in a practical and realistic context.

(e) Personality

The personality component of the assessment process is a two-part Occupational Personality Questionnaire (OPQ) that assesses three major areas of behaviour: Relationships with People; Thinking Style; Feelings and Emotions.

These three areas are in turn broken down into 9 sub-scales and a total of 31 individual scales.

The two parts of the questionnaire are the Concept Model 3 (CM3) and the Concept Model 5 (CM5). Concept 3 is a three-option multiple-choice format in which the questions are primarily concerned with direct work-related behaviour. Concept 5 is a five-option multiple-choice format in which the options range from 'strongly agree' to 'strongly disagree' and the statements include views and attitudes as well as behaviour.

APPENDIX 3. STATISTICS

Measure	Mean	SD	Range	Number
Age	27.269	3.826	20 - 36	234
Flying Hrs	3047.318	1397.906	694 - 8959	233
PAT/Skills Total	142.029	19.193	96 - 180	136
INSB (Stanine)	7.243	1.358	2 - 9	136
SMA (Stanine)	8.037	1.336	1 - 9	136
CVT (Stanine)	5.346	1.626	1 - 9	136
Simulator Check	4.116	0.641	2 - 5	233
Flight Check	3.944	0.487	3 - 5	189
Verbal Concepts (VA1)	22.809	4.181	13 - 33	199
Number Series (NA2)	18.236	3.486	10 - 27	199
Diagram. Reasoning (DT8)	21.070	4.154	11 - 33	199
Total (VA1/NA2/DT8)	61.975	9.110	36 - 88	199
Verb. Crit. Reasoning (VA3)	38.698	6.048	19 - 52	199
Numer. Crit. Reason. (NA4)	18.984	6.421	5 - 38	190
Personality (Stens)				
R1	5.854	1.854	1 - 10	199
R2	5.970	1.817	1 - 10	199
R3	5.362	2.000	1 - 10	199
R4	5.709	1.852	1 - 10	199
R5	5.905	1.866	1 - 10	199
R6	6.055	1.801	1 - 9	199

APPENDIX 3 (Continued)

Measure	Mean	SD	Range	Number
R7	5.583	2.011	1 - 9	199
R8	5.683	2.068	1 - 10	199
R9	5.799	1.910	1 - 10	199
T1	5.779	2.038	1 - 9	199
T2	6.161	1.903	1 - 10	199
T3	5.085	2.052	1 - 10	199
T4	5.638	2.015	1 - 10	199
T5	5.477	1.969	1 - 10	199
T6	5.633	2.099	1 - 10	199
T7	5.683	2.014	1 - 10	199
T8	5.618	2.173	1 - 10	199
T9	5.784	1.775	1 - 9	199
T10	5.673	1.839	1 - 9	199
T11	5.442	1.940	1 - 10	199
F1	5.859	1.944	1 - 10	199
F2	5.166	1.863	1 - 9	199
F3	5.633	1.918	1 - 10	199
F4	5.648	1.852	1 - 10	199
F5	5.387	1.841	1 - 9	199
F6	5.779	1.910	1 - 10	199
F7	5.638	1.995	1 - 10	199
F8	5.317	1.871	2 - 10	199
F9	5.101	2.038	1 - 10	199
F10	5.422	1.978	1 - 10	199
D1	5.663	1.926	1 - 10	199
Initial Course	90.886	4.641	69 - 99.5	229
Type Course	93.103	4.288	80 - 99	229
FBS	2.502	0.425	1 - 3.5	202
Simulator	2.823	0.521	1 - 4	186
FT9	2.788	0.344	2 - 3.5	186

2

Selection of ab initio pilot candidates: The SAS system
Hans Gordon

ABSTRACT

It seems necessary to invite almost 1500 candidates to a preliminary screening procedure if you want to find 100 suitable ab initio pilot candidates. In this chapter I will try to explain some tips – and traps – of the selection programme as it is used by SAS in Scandinavia.

INTRODUCTION

I work primarily within a Scandinavian consultant organization called SIAP (Scandinavian Institute of Aviation Psychology). The organization started originally in 1951, when the late Professor Arne Trankell was hired by the recently established SAS with the aim of developing a psychological technique for the selection of airline pilots.

It was not long before the group of psychologists was formed into a special team, trained by Professor Trankell. The technique used was not a revolutionary one: it consisted of a thorough investigation from many points of view, where traditional and standardized tests were just one of a large number of complex sources of information, all put together and judged and evaluated by the psychologists. Psychometric and psychotechnical tests were mixed together with clinical approaches from the psychologists. The most important part of the investigation was certainly the interview.

Interviewing – viewing inter, or in between, or beyond and behind – demands of the psychologist a lot of effort and special skills. The interview acts as the central scenery, where every item of information could be transferred into hypothesis – and tested. The interview situation could – if the examiner is skilful enough – be looked upon as the melting pot, where the psychologist has to evaluate every single datum, being flexible enough to correct himself if needed, taking nothing for granted, hunting for more information if he cannot understand what is shown – and slowly building a picture of the person, just like building a house, starting with the basement, the basics, following the development upwards and outwards. This is a difficult job, and I will return to it later.

I had the opportunity and privilege to join the SIAP team in 1964 (it was then called IIAP), and since then I have been rather active in my work, most of it being done for SAS Airline.

Every airline has created its own method of pilot selection. In SAS the traditional and ordinary way is this: a pilot applicant of interest to SAS – and that means that he or she must have a certain number of hours in the air, at least 300 on multi-engined aircraft, the special Commercial Pilot Licences in order, the age preferably not above 35 – is first interviewed by two separate company representatives, including at least one pilot, in separate rooms. Afterwards a discussion is held between the interviewers, and a decision is made whether the candidate will be accepted for a final selection or not.

Now it is the psychologists' turn. First is a written group test battery, including a life description in own handwriting, then a multiple interview situation, where each candidate has to pass two separate psychologists and two separate company representatives. The two psychologists make their ratings on a scale of a wide variety of personality capacities and other dynamic personal forces. Furthermore each psychologist writes a rather complex report on every single candidate. The report consists of a wide range of information concerning social patterns, personal events, former career at school and work, family life, attitudes and overall behaviour. One of the two psychologists has the final responsibility for the concluding remarks and the prediction to be made, which means that the psychologists must meet and discuss each case before the final board meeting is held.

It might be of interest to examine the outcome of the psychological predictions. This figure is not a new one – it stems from 1978, when Professor Trankell conducted a large evaluation study of the SAS pilot selection. During the period 1951-1978 a total of 1265 pilots had been employed. The number dismissed due to incapacity during training or later performance was 62 (4.9%). Most of the dismissal cases were found among those candidates hired by SAS against the advice of the psychologists.

Table 1. Employed and dismissed pilots 1951-1978

Psychologists' prediction score	Number employed	Number dismissed	Rate of dismissal
8-9	33	0	0.0%
7	233	4	1.8%
6	484	19	3.9%
5	468	20	4.3%
4	42	8	19.0%
1-3	15	11	73.3%

There has been no detailed follow-up study during the last ten years, but it is a well known fact that there have been only a few dismissed cases during that time.

THE START OF AB INITIO PILOT SELECTION

The selection of young ab initio pilot candidates started in 1977, when the Swedish Air Force created a new reserve officer training programme with the intention of making this group attractive to the commercial airline companies. SAS was one of the main participants in the project, assisting the Air Force with training facilities as well as asking SIAP to join the selection procedure. The project went on for four years. The selection of the applicants was divided into two main steps: the first was basic screening, conducted by the psychologists from the Air Force; the second was handled by SIAP for a narrower investigation of the candidates.

The result was promising: 37 of 44 candidates with SIAP scorings ranging from 5 upwards (recommended students) reached the main goal, which was to succeed during the training programme and become employed by SAS. Only 2 of 17 candidates with poor scorings (4 or less) made the same progress. The bi-serial correlation coefficient was as high as 0.84.

In 1984 the first Scandinavian Government Flying Training School for Commercial Pilots started in Sweden. Due to the outcome of the reserve officer project it was decided that the selection procedure would be organized in the same pattern: Air Force and SIAP in co-operation.

A more complete evaluation study of the results from the training in the Swedish Government Flying Training School has not yet been made. However, of 192 accepted candidates there were until May 1989 only 3 drop-outs.

In 1987 the need for new pilots in SAS was dramatically increased. At the same time the former pilot source – the Scandinavian Air Forces – became much more reluctant to let their experienced pilots join the commercial airline companies. The Government Flying Training School had not yet developed full capacity.

SAS then made the historic decision to start its own ab initio training programme. After examining some well known private flying training schools, the choice was made in favour of the North American Institute of Aviation (NAIA) in South Carolina, USA. Necessary contacts were made, contracts were signed and a special training programme was created and developed in co-operation between NAIA and the SAS Flight Academy.

The selection of young ab initio candidates was regarded as a highly delicate matter. It was now more important than ever to reach and select 'the right stuff'. Experiences from the SAS Pilot Recruitment section, the SAS Flight Academy and SIAP were brought together, ending up in a new selection procedure. This is divided into four separate steps, and in the following I will give you a brief description of each one of the steps, including some remarks on tips – and traps – that could occur along the road.

Step 1

The first step consists of a screening system, based upon written tests. The basic notion is that an acceptable candidate has to pass a certain level on an overall test profile. It might be acceptable if he – or she – drops down a bit in one or two or even three of the tests given. That depends on how the general picture looks.

The tests are in general quite common. We are using a lot of tasks related to inductive intelligence, technical comprehension, mathematical and numerical understanding, speed and quality of visual and auditory perception, spatial orientation ability and so on. Several of our tests were created and developed by ourselves. Step 1 lasts from 0830 until about 1500.

During this step we do not use any machines or new technical equipment. It is just ordinary pencil-and-paper work, where the tests are manually evaluated during the day. About 15 minutes after the last test has been collected we are ready to discuss and determine the outcome. After a short break the candidates receive the result: 'The following are invited to Step 2.'

Traps: A lot of tests used in this field have undergone routine analysis by statistical means: inter-correlations, reliability and validity analysis and so forth. The results are not always overwhelmingly impressive. Some of the tests that could be bought in the professional open market are not proved to deal with airline pilot candidates but are still considered to be of value. One of the main reasons to use all these psychometric methods is of an economic nature: it is easy to handle a huge number of candidates in this way.

Tip: To strengthen the general test profile and its value with respect to the requirements of an airline pilot, it could be useful to organize the working day as a flight simulation. It is, for example, possible to create a day of working with tests where the energy inputs from the candidates correspond to a flight situation. That means that the result of the tests could be looked upon not only as a single psychometric value in itself, but as an effect of what has been distributed to the candidates, following a special order. As an example: a day could start a bit soft, not too difficult, just warming up the brain. After a while you just have to speed everything up, to be careful and concentrated. Later on, you may relax a bit, pressure not so high, when suddenly you have to use every part of your energy system to make a happy landing.

Giving instructions to the candidates, it could even be of a certain value – at least a face value – to indicate that this is what you need when you have to deal with strenuous pilot work.

Table 2 shows an example of the test organization.

Table 2. Organizing a group test battery

Flight procedure	Examples of test
Flight planning	Organization test
	Mathematical problems
Pre-flight inspection	Speed and quality of perception
	Technical comprehension
Start and climb	Visual and auditory perception
	Spatial orientation
Cruise	Aspects of personality: questionnaire,
	life description, verbal fluency
Approach and descent	Inductive intelligence
	Concentration ability
	Simultaneous capacity
	Spatial orientation
Landing	Visual and auditory perception
	Exactitude

Step 2

Step 2 is a thorough psychological investigation made by an experienced and well trained aviation psychologist. The training includes not only a profound orientation about the qualifications needed for an airline pilot, but even more the demands of the psychological work to be done.

The main instrument is the interview, where the psychologist tries to study several dynamic forces in the personality area of the candidate: how he is able to use his resources during various circumstances, how he relates to people, how he has reached various developmental steps in his emotional and mental life etc. The psychologist is during this step also checking some traditional factors of importance, like simultaneous capacity, resistance to panic reactions and so on.

Collecting a broad spectrum of data makes it necessary to let the psychologist work through all these parts of information. This is done after the candidate has left the room. The psychologist will then write an analytic report about the findings, also trying to explain why it is this and not that and so on, ending with a prediction about the abilities and character of the candidate in relation to the airline work. The complete process − from the start of Step 2 until the predictions are made − takes about two hours per candidate, no more.

Traps: Despite the educational level of the psychologist it is always necessary to be reminded of the human mind of the investigator: he or she has certainly some ideal inner objects, created more out of fantasies than out of real experience. He or she has certainly also some inner denied objects, or threat figures – and when meeting someone who looks similar to those a typical unfair judgement could appear as an effect.

Let me mention two examples: an elderly male psychologist has an unconscious wish not to be overruled by a young, bright 'son'. Meeting a young, male candidate with oppositional expressions and clear intelligence in his eyes could end up with a low prediction score. The other example: the female psychologist who does not want to compare herself with young female, attractive candidates is happy to meet girls who in many ways want to appear as boys or young men. Overestimating their abilities means the boyish girls receive good prediction scores.

Tips: Everyone has a conscious conception of his or her own motives, personality structure and ability strength – even though the self-image is now and then unclear and unstable. In the same sense: everyone has in-built unconscious dynamic forces, urging for actions and satisfactions. To investigate a young candidate, his or her motives, efficiency of resources in various situations and so on demands an analysis of the development not only of the cognitive and intellectual functions but of psychosexual level and stability as well. This is facilitated by a thorough interview around the life story, the pictures of important family members, important memories from various growing-up periods and so forth. A special request directed to the psychologist: even you have an unconscious mind. Just think of it - and re-check your final assessments.

Step 3

It is advisable to believe in the assessments made by an experienced psychologist. It is advisable not to believe any psychologist. Both statements could be true. Just to strengthen the net, step 3 includes a re-check made by another psychologist in the team.

The promising candidates are sent to this step and are investigated by one psychologist (a new one) and two separate SAS representatives. There are thus three interviewing stations that have to be passed. The SAS model does not include any group or panel interview. There are reasons to believe that a more comfortable and relaxed conversation could reveal more of both hidden strengths and questionable attributes of each candidate.

After this step the Recruitment Board Meeting collects all relevant information about the candidates and makes decisions of acceptance for the final step, number 4.

Traps: There is a slight risk that the psychologists try to validate their assessments by listening to what the experienced recruitment people from the airline company have found – and vice versa: there is a slight risk that the airline personnel first want to know the psychological findings before they state their own conclusions. Underneath lies an ordinary conflict or competition-like situation. No one wants to risk the shame of being wrong.

Tip: Albert Einstein once stated that only when the observers of a particular object or field of objects are moving in the same direction and with the same speed will the observations reach the same measures or values. Do not even try to reach the same picture. Look at the value of having three or even more pictures of the same person – each one is showing something of importance for the predictions that have to be made.

Step 4

The candidates invited to step 4 are all assessed as promising cases, in their capacities as well as in their personality structures. There are, however, circumstances or 'hidden factors' that are difficult to control. First of all: young ab initio candidates are often still in a dynamic developmental phase where a lot of intra- and inter-psychic forces make them swing in attitudes, beliefs, motivation and efficiency of using basic resources. That is why the SAS Flight Academy and SIAP in co-operation developed step 4, also called the Pre-Course (prior to the NAIA training).

The Pre-Course consists of 7-8 days of intensive work at the SAS Flight Academy in Stockholm, Sweden. The aims are specified in the following points: after finishing the course the candidates will have (a) had detailed and quite complete information about the working environment of a SAS commercial pilot, including modern training facilities of all kinds; (b) understood the demands and requirements of a commercial airline pilot, both in general terms and for SAS specifically; (c) demonstrated the ability and willingness to learn the basics of flying theory such as aerodynamics, important flight instruments, engine power and elementary operational procedures; (d) had basic knowledge about two important para-technical areas: human factors and medical fitness; (e) demonstrated the ability and willingness to act according to given instructions, particularly when forced to handle elementary flight simulator operations; and (f) demonstrated a social tact and team work ability related to the requirements.

To reach these goals experienced flight instructors give lessons, introducing modern educational techniques such as computer-based training systems and video techniques. To check abilities and motivation they arrange examinations of the theoretical parts, and – above all – they test the skills of the candidates in a heavy jet flight simulator. The candidates then just follow more elementary operational instructions. They also pass a special psychological group training programme, where it is possible to detect odd or strained behaviour in various socially related 'games'.

One important point with the Pre-Course is that the arranged situation invites the candidates to get a close look at the pilot workstations, thus having the opportunity to test their own motivation. The clearly announced recommendation is that each one who feels ambivalent or hesitant or negative in his attitude to the test environment should step forward and talk to one of the instructors or psychologists about these feelings.

Immediately after Pre-Course the board of the recruitment section makes the final decisions on the candidates. The whole procedure ends with a de-briefing, where the candidates – one by one – get a thorough indication of how he, or she, has been assessed. For the lucky ones the next stop is NAIA, USA.

Trap: It is very easy to get the idea that the almost real situation during Pre-Course brings the real pilot candidate to the surface, and to overestimate its validity. Psychological tests are often good enough, but here is the real thing. How could a candidate who could not learn how to take control in the flight simulator ever become a really good airline pilot?

Tips: Before the final conclusions are reached and decisions made it is of great importance to check and re-check with the findings from Steps 1, 2 and 3. The candidate might be a slow learner, whose basic skills just slumber beneath an attitude of inexperience. In the long run he or she will become 'a winner'. The value of the observations from step 4 will certainly increase if it is possible to involve an aviation psychologist in the flight simulator part of the programme. We have done so in the SAS/NAIA project, where the flight instructor and the psychologist take notes, making ratings in important behaviour variables, and later discuss each case.

EPILOGUE

There is also a Step 5 .... and 6 and 7 and 8. Step 5 is the Flying training period at NAIA. Step 6 is the advanced multi-jet-engine training at SAS Flight Academy. Step 7 is the Route Training Programme operated by the Chief Pilots at the Crew Base. Step 8 is the first year of employment as a fresh F/O.

None of those steps is traditionally described as a selection step. But selection and training are two closely connected concepts. There will be no successful training with candidates below a certain standard. There will not be a successful conclusion to the selection procedures without a very good training programme.

The future will show how the project will be evaluated. So far we have the figures for the outcome of the SAS/NAIA project shown in Table 3. The data are approximated from the start of the project in spring 1987. The approximation is made from several selection steps – from 1987 to spring 1989. The first Pre-Course took place in November 1987. The training programme at NAIA started in December the same year and ended in August 1988. During spring 1989 the first young ab initio pilots were released from SAS Flight Academy. At the time of writing, the first route training programme is not yet finished, but the aim is that within a couple of months there will be a base release of sixteen new SAS MD-80 pilots, all coming from the first NAIA group.

Table 3. The outcome of the SAS/NAIA screening

	Percentage accepted to next step	Percentage left
Step 1	54%	54.0%
Step 2	31%	16.7%
Step 3	52%	8.7%
Step 4	82%	7.1%
Step 5	97%	6.9%
Step 6	97%	6.7%
Step 7	?	?
Step 8	?	?

From the table above it is possible to make the following conclusions: If you want 20 ab initio pilots you will have to invite at least 299 candidates for a first screening procedure. If you want 50 pilots you will have to call at least 746 candidates. If you want 100 pilots you will have to examine at least 1492 candidates in the first screening procedure.

3

Organizational aspects of non-technical programmes
André Droog

ABSTRACT

This paper is about the effectiveness of organizations and the conditions for individual and group effectiveness. These conditions are, in the opinion of the author, essential considerations in the initiation of non-technical training programmes and also have consequences for the policy of the management of an ab initio training flying school.

INTRODUCTION

KLM takes in about 40 pilots every year from the RLS, the main Dutch flying school, which still belongs to the Dutch government but will probably become a KLM flying school in the very near future. When entering KLM the ab initio trainees have followed a 200-hour flying course at our school: 70 hours basic training on the Cessna 152, 90 hours advanced training on the Beechcraft B-33 Bonanza (including the IF Rating) and 40 hours final training on the Cessna C-500 Citation (including type-rating and route-training). All flying training is supported by simulator training; since 1988 the school has had a glass cockpit C-500 Citation simulator.

Crew-concept training is given from the advanced phase onwards. The RLS has a non-technical programme to support the crew-co-operation training, to enhance safety awareness, and to stimulate personality development. This programme pays attention to communication, team building (Outward Bound training), decision making, and leadership. Within both KLM and RLS there is concern to develop non-technical training programmes further and to integrate them in the total training programme.

THE NEED FOR INTEGRATION

Why integrate? Organizations develop. They grow and change their internal structures constantly. During their lifetime they experience a lot of

29

quantitative and qualitative change. Three stages of development of an organization can be seen (Lievegoed, 1977; see Figure 1).

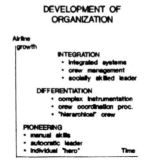

Figure 1. Stages in the development of an organization

First comes the pioneer. He discovers a consumer need and creatively answers this need by making a product. He starts his own small enterprise. The pioneer is primarily interested in the economic-technical performance of his firm. His leadership is autocratic and charismatic, and the structure of the organization is simple. Communications with the few personnel are direct and problems are solved by improvisation. Flexibility is high, one feels 'one big family' and customers are known personally. Customers are part of the 'closed dynamic' system. However, changes in the environment (technical advancement, competition, growing market) make the pioneer firm vulnerable (profits lower, customers complain) and a crisis may result. A new structure becomes necessary: if the crisis is well understood the organization enters the phase of differentiation.

During the differentiation phase the organization uses the principles of scientific management to grow and stay alive. Rationality is the leading principle. Mechanization, standardization, specialization, and co-ordination are introduced. Machines and standardized methods enter the organization. Specialization of tasks creates the need for co-ordination by formal supervision. Planning and technical training become part of the management tools. The integration of people's actions, however, is based on formal hierarchical principles. The organization becomes more bureaucratic. Control of the internal structure is the main preoccupation of the management in this phase. The attention of the leaders is directed inward, towards the internal organization rather than the environment.

The strength of the differentiation phase is the rational, 'technical' approach, both to production and organization. But a second crisis will result and the weaknesses of this rational organization will manifest themselves when further growth occurs. Flexibility is low because of formalization and bureaucracy, and there are problems of co-ordination because of too much specialization. Departments are cherished by their chiefs as 'little empires' and have their own norms and goals. There are too many functional levels. The market has become 'anonymous': the customer is seen as instrumental to the firm instead of the firm being there for the customer. The third phase of development, the integration phase, must start if the organization wants to grow and survive.

The importance of the integration phase is the development of the social sub-system of the organization. In other words, in this phase the social system is developed and integrated in the already developed economic and technical systems. This integration is a step by step process. If successful, the people in the organization 'can and will act intelligently, with an eye to the whole of the organization' (Lievegoed, 1977). In this phase the management directs its attention outward and seeks feedback from the environment about the quality of the service and products. Its mentality becomes client-oriented. The organization is seen as an input-throughput-output system rather than as a hierarchy. Permanent training directed at professionalism of all people in the organization becomes part of the system. Departments become process-oriented instead of hierarchy-oriented. The organization must become flexible on all levels, an open system which is constantly learning.

Many organizations have more or less gone through this economic-technical-social development, including the big airlines, most of which find themselves in some sort of integration process today. The most recent development is the formation of airline networks, as is the present practice of KLM to integrate captaincy training and assessment of captaincy into its Line-Oriented Flight Training and Type Recurrent Training.

So, why integrate technical and non-technical activities? Because by integration organizations increase their overall competence and effectiveness. Increasing complexity and changing markets demand goal-orientation and motivation of all people in the organization and both technical and social competence. Before giving attention to how this can be achieved, we will consider the conditions for organizational effectiveness.

INDIVIDUAL AND ORGANIZATIONAL EFFECTIVENESS

The core activities of any system are (1) to achieve its objectives, (2) to maintain its internal environment, and (3) to adapt to, and maintain control over, the relevant external environment. How well the system accomplishes these core activities over time, under different conditions and in any given situation, indicates its competence and effectiveness (Argyris, 1973).

Argyris mentions a number of criteria that may be used to evaluate the effectiveness of a system (e.g. available and understandable information that is usable to the system; problems that are solved and decisions made without recurring when within the control of the system) and also identifies conditions causing individuals and groups to behave most competently. The more these conditions are approximated, the greater the probability that the individuals or groups will meet the competence criteria. The conditions for the individual are: self-acceptance, confirmation, and essentiality.

Self-acceptance is the degree to which a person has confidence in himself and regards himself favourably. The higher the self-acceptance, the more he values himself. The more he values himself, the more he will value others.

A person experiences confirmation when others experience him as he experiences himself. Confirmation is needed to validate one's view of oneself. Everyone experiences the world through his own set of biases and will tend to see only what his own self permits or encourages him to see. The possibility of error is therefore always present and this built-in potential for error creates a basic posture of uncertainty and self-doubt and a tendency to enquire into the accuracy of one's perception or sense of reality. Hence the need for confirmation. The more frequent the confirmation, the greater the confidence in one's potential to behave competently.

Essentiality means that, the more the individual is able to use his central abilities and express his central needs, the greater will be his feelings of essentiality to himself and the system. The more essential he feels, the more committed he will tend to be to the system and to its effectiveness.

One of the most effective ways to help individuals increase their self-acceptance, confirmation, and essentiality is to create conditions for psychological success. Psychological success occurs when: (a) the individual is able to define his own goals; (b) these goals are related to his central needs, abilities and values; (c) the person defines the path to these goals; and (d) their achievement represents a realistic level of aspiration, which means a challenge or a risk that requires hitherto unused, untested, abilities.

Behaviours contributing to interpersonal and technical competence are: (a) being open to ideas and feelings of others and those from within oneself; (b) experimenting with new ideas and feelings, and helping others to do so; and (c) stimulating these behaviours in such a way that one contributes to the norms of individuality (instead of conformity), concern (rather than competition), and trust (instead of mistrust).

Groups increase their effectiveness to the extent that the leader and the members facilitate the conditions, behaviours and norms mentioned above. This is best done by: (a) shared leadership; (b) reduction of the gap between leader and members; (c) attention of the group members to group processes to reduce blocks; and (d) concern being expressed by group members for the effectiveness of the group whenever they feel this is necessary.

What are the consequences of all this for ab initio training and flying school management?

CONSEQUENCES FOR TRAINING

The purpose of crew training is to increase the effectiveness of both individual crew members and the crew as a whole. Training will be most effective and efficient when integrated as much as possible by the following means: (a) the flight-instructors train both the technical and the non-technical element during flying or simulated flying, and (b) they are supported by a non-technical training staff which (1) is able to support them if learning problems or interpersonal problems arise, and (2) sets up a non-technical programme from which trainees can benefit by learning to know themselves and develop practical and relevant skills.

For (a) it will be necessary to train the instructors in having an eye for the human aspect and give them tools to assess the strengths and weaknesses of crew members with regard, for example, to communication or leadership. Such a system will be developed with KLM in the near future.

With regard to the learning problems of (b[1]), especially the problems trainees may have with decision making, management, team-work or captaincy, we should keep in mind that real learning is double-loop learning. This term must be explained. Learning occurs under two conditions: when a match is achieved between the plan for action and the actual outcome of the action, and when a mismatch between intention and outcome is corrected and turned into a match. Whenever an error is detected and corrected without questioning or altering the underlying values of the individual trainee, crew, or organization, the learning is single-loop. Real learning is double-loop learning which occurs when mismatches are corrected by first examining and altering the 'governing variables' and then the action, which means that one has to discover the underlying reasons for error and slow learning progress (Figure 2).

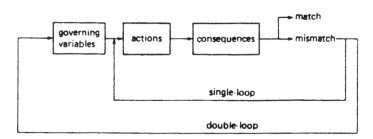

Figure 2. Single- and double-loop learning (Argyris, 1988)

For reasons of integration, a non-technical training programme should include as many as possible real-life situations as practice material. It should also create the conditions for psychological success and help to teach trainees to express their individuality (stimulate expressivity) within a system that very strongly favours conformity and compliance. It should stimulate mutual trust, self-acceptance and the learning of the skills of being open, flexible and positive.

The non-technical training syllabus at the RLS needs some expansion and restructuring. The aim is to make it a thread (not a threat) throughout the whole course. Starting with the Outward Bound training (which touches upon themes like physical endurance, trust, communication, team-work and leadership) we can continue with communication, decision making, and leadership, and in particular crew management. Currently these themes are all in a three-day programme, but they deserve more attention, although the extra time seems not yet to be available.

In the Decision-making module both the rational and emotional sides of the decision-making process must be the focus of attention. Janis and Mann (1977) developed a conflict model of decision making which could be the basis for practical training. Both learning the rational decision-making process (facts, problem solving, choice of alternative) and discovering one's own values, hazardous thoughts, risk-taking behaviour, and stress reactions are essential.

In the Leadership module special attention must be paid to conflict, one of the elementary phenomena in social and organizational life. The trainees' 'theories about effective action' when dealing with others and their defences against error, anxiety or criticism can be discovered and discussed; those values or behaviours favourable to good leadership and those leading to win-lose or win-win situations in dealing with conflicts can be identified. Then strategies can be trained, for example those of saying things in the right words and at the right moment.

CONSEQUENCES FOR MANAGEMENT

One of the tasks of the management will be to install and stimulate programmes that (a) lead to integration, (b) contribute to psychological success of groups and individuals in the organization, and (c) contribute to the norms of individuality, concern, and trust among groups in the school organization.

CONCLUSION

The pilot, being 'in the loop' of a technical, social and economic system will benefit from knowledge and skills in these fields (Figure 3). The effect of non-technical training must be that of widening his scope, increasing total-system awareness and introducing more skilful leadership. The organization or trainer is an interventionist who, to produce effectiveness, must facilitate personal development by integrated technical and non-technical programmes and by creating the conditions for effectiveness mentioned above.

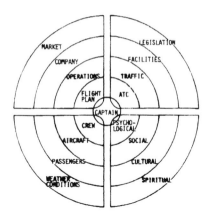

Figure 3. The pilot 'in the loop'

REFERENCES

Argyris, C. (1973). *Intervention Theory and Method.* Massachusetts: Addison-Wesley Publishing Company.

Argyris, C. (1988). Problems in producing usable knowledge for implementing liberating alternatives. In D. E. Bell et al. (Eds.), *Decision Making.* Pp 540-561. Cambridge: Cambridge University Press.

Janis, I.L. and Mann, L. (1977). *Decision Making: A Psychological Analysis of Conflict, Choice and Commitment.* New York: Free Press.

Lievegoed, B.C.J. (1977). *Organisaties in Ontwikkeling.* Rotterdam: Lemniscaat.

4

DLR selection of air traffic control applicants: Predictive validity
Hinnerk Eißfeldt

INTRODUCTION

The main field of work of the Department of Aviation and Space Psychology in the German Aerospace Research Establishment (DLR) is the psychological selection of operators for complex technical systems. By means of valid selection methods the efficiency and reliability of these systems can be improved significantly. Most of the selection methods in use were originally developed for pilot selection, since the DLR has been in charge of the Lufthansa ab initio pilot selection for more than 30 years. In the last ten years the selection methods have been applied in modified versions to other areas of aviation in West Germany. Since 1982 the DLR has been in charge of the psychological selection of Air Traffic Control (ATC) personnel for the Federal Administration of Air Navigation Services (BFS).

THE SELECTION CONCEPT

The task of the psychological selection of Air Traffic Controllers is first to predict the success of an applicant in ATC training and second to guarantee that the checked-out Air Traffic Controller is in the long run able to cope with the high demands in his job until he reaches retirement age.

In addition to operational skills, aspects of inter-personal behaviour and emotional stability have to be taken into account. Therefore the psychological selection of ATC staff cannot rely on only a few specific methods; a multi-modal evaluation is needed covering biographical data as well as performance and personality tests. The efficient application of valid methods in personnel selection requires continuous scientific scrutiny if the selection system is to satisfy all demands optimally. The applied test methods are regularly checked for psychometric quality criteria such as reliability of measurement and, as soon as possible, they have to be checked for predictive validity as well.

THE SELECTION CRITERIA

The following list shows traits assessed in the selection procedure:

Performance

Basic knowledge: English, Technical Comprehension, Mathematico-Logical Thinking

Operational Aptitudes: Memory, Perception and Attention, Spatial Orientation (all measured in two modalities: auditory and visual), and Multiple Task Capacity

Personality

Achievement-Oriented Traits: Motivation, Rigidity, Mobility, Vitality

Inter-personal Behaviour: Extraversion, Dominance, Aggressiveness, Empathy

Stress Resistance: Emotional Stability

To reach an optimum of redundancy, every specific trait is measured by several items of information from the test battery. To standardize the decision criteria among the various members of the selection board, the decisions have to follow some basic rules:

1. The total profile of ability and personality traits is relevant;
2. For performance tests, scores below average relative to the normative group are critical;
3. Extreme high or low scores are equally critical for most of the personality and motivation scales;
4. If in the redundant test system a clear performance and/or personality deficiency is revealed, the applicant will be rejected despite all other test results.

THE SELECTION PROCEDURE

A sequential procedure consisting of four steps is used in the ATC selection for economic reasons as well as to meet the demands of test fairness: passing the full selection procedure takes an applicant four days plus medical examination, so it is in his own interests to be released from the procedure as soon as severe deficits in required aptitudes are recognized. The first step of psychological testing is called Pre-Selection and consists of a battery of 8 paper/pencil tests. It provides the first information about basic traits of ATC applicants. At the end of each Pre-Selection campaign all applicants who seem to be suitable for further investigation (40-45% of the total group) are invited to the Main Selection phase, which consists of three different parts:

Part I : 11 additional paper/pencil tests plus Vigilance test, administered in groups of a maximum of 15 applicants;

Part II : Apparatus tests plus English oral examination;

Part III: Interview in front of the selection board and final decision directly afterwards. The board comprises one senior controller (chairman), two experienced ATCOs from BFS and two aviation psychologists from DLR with an advisory function.

At the end of each Part (I-III) results are discussed by the board members and applicants are dismissed if their aptitudes do not meet the requirements. At the end of Part III successful applicants are medically examined by a specialist in aviation medicine. The whole selection procedure reduces the number of applicants finally accepted to about 10-12% of the total group. Figure 1 demonstrates how the different steps in the Main Selection reduce the number of applicants if 100 pre-selected applicants begin the Main Selection phase.

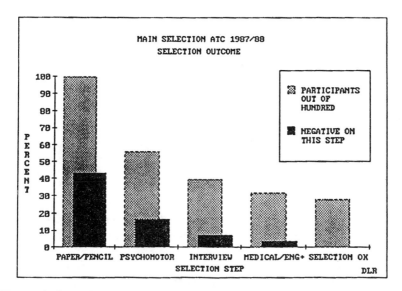

Figure 1. Selection ratio at different steps of the Main Selection phase during the selection of Air Traffic Controllers. Percentages computed on the data of N = 865 applicants in 1987/88

The DLR Department of Aviation and Space Psychology has been selecting Air Traffic Controllers since 1982. Figure 2 shows the number of applicants for the years 1982-1988.

Since 1982 a total of 475 candidates have taken up training; 201 of them have meanwhile finished the three years of basic training. Thirty-six applicants belonging to this group of 201 failed in ATC training.

ATC TRAINING STRUCTURE

Within the Federal Republic of Germany air traffic controllers are members of the high level civil service. Thus the training of air traffic controllers takes place at the department of air traffic control integrated within the 'College for Public Administration of the FRG'. Structure and training time follow a unique definition that is equal for all careers in the civil service. The training of air traffic controllers comprises an interchange of theoretical studies and practical training. A general view is given in Figure 3.

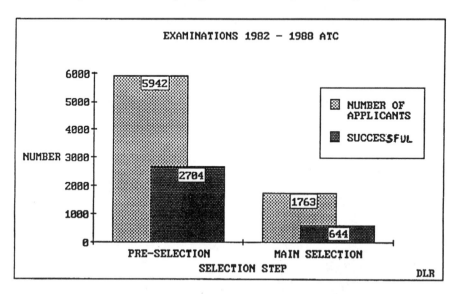

Figure 2. Number of applicants and number successful at the different steps of the selection of ATC applicants for the years 1982-1988

At the end of three years of studies the career examination is held, during which the aptitudes and skills for the specific career in the civil service are checked. For air traffic controllers this examination comprises simulator checks, written tests, and an oral exam. During the career examination the trainee gives evidence that he has all the required knowledge, aptitudes, and skills necessary to gain all relevant licences. Following the career examination the trainee is transferred to one of the local ATC-units where he continues his on the job training until he gains the required local licences. The training period until the air traffic controller is fully checked out on his working positions ranges from 18 to 24 months.

CRITERIA FOR TRAINING SUCCESS

The following list describes examinations during the training of Air Traffic Controllers, which are taken as criteria for training success:

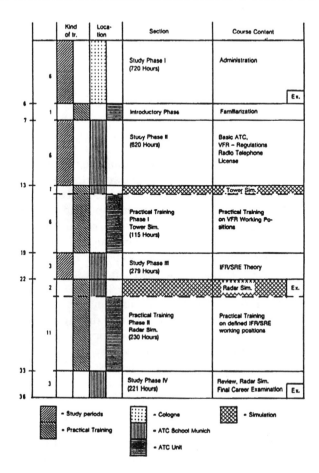

Figure 3. Training scheme for Air Traffic Controllers
used from 1982 to 1988

Examination 1 (6 months)
Written tests on aspects of law, civil service, can be repeated once, no-go item.

Examination 2 (24 months)
Practical tests at a radar simulation system on ATC problems, can be repeated once, no-go item.

Radar simulation (34 months)
Practical part of the final career examination, three runs on different working positions, each run is no-go item, can be repeated once.

Final examination average score.
Represents all relevant assessments and examinations in theoretical and practical parts of the training for successful trainees.

Pass/fail
Success in training (yes/no).

FAILURE RATE

As long as no criterion data were available, the failure rates in different steps of training were the only empirical indicator for the usefulness of the psychological selection system. They showed decreases in failure rates compared to ATC trainees who were selected before 1982.

Those 36 ATC trainees who were selected by the DLR test system and could not pass training failed at different stages and for different reasons. Detailed investigation shows that only about half of them (17) failed for the reason of poor performance (mainly they were not able to cope with the high demands of practical training and examination). The other 19 trainees sometimes even had superior performance abilities; these drop-outs were basically linked to aspects of motivation, as they left ATC training mostly to take up other careers in aviation as pilots or dispatchers, or even in other fields of occupation such as medicine or other sciences. Even if the total number of failures (36) is taken into account, compared to failure rates reported from other European countries (EUROCONTROL, 1988) this failure rate of 18% seems to be very low.

RESULTS

In a first validation study covering a seven-year period from 1982 to 1988, a total of 201 ATC-trainees were followed up after their acceptance in the psychological selection. Five training criteria (examination 1, examination 2, radar simulation, final average score and pass/fail) were measured against a battery of predictor variables, consisting of 20 unweighted test results which represent all the traits assessed in the selection of ATC applicants. Table 1 shows the results for each criterion of training success.

DISCUSSION

Every validation study has to face several difficulties on its way. In particular, the validation of a test system that is already in use is handicapped by the well known problems of restriction of range in the test results. Another obstacle is the restriction in the magnitude of correlation coefficients, because all test performance results have to be expressed in standardized values to cover some slight changes in special test items that cannot be avoided in a test system that is in use over a long period. In this study STANINE scores are used as basic data for the computations, so the values of the multiple correlation coefficient R shown in Table 1 have to be seen as underestimation of the real values.

Table 1. Validities of the test battery against five different criteria for training success. Multiple correlation coefficient (R) values, significance of R, percent of correctly classified cases in discriminant analysis

Training Criteria	Multiple Regression (R)	Sign.	Discriminant Analysis (correct classified)	N
Exam 1	.55	.005	78 %	196
Exam 2	.51	.041	67 %	187
Radar Sim.	.61	.001	67 %	175
Fin. Av. score	.61	.003	70 %	162
Pass/Fail	.43	ns	69 %	201

Besides the problems discussed above, this study must face the fact that there are different reasons for failure in training. As applicants who leave ATC Training of their own free will have to repay some of their training costs, there are good reasons for trainees to fake their failure, i.e. to wait until BFS has to dismiss them. That might be the reason for the low, non-significant R value of the pass/fail criterion. In fact, it should rather be named the 'pass/fail-withdrawal' criterion. Although there is strong evidence for faking failure in some cases, as long as no proof is found all these cases remain included and are handled like all other data in this study. The results of the discriminant analysis for the different training criteria show that the selection results can predict training success more in the theoretical phases of training than in the practical periods. The multiple correlation coefficient R for the final examination average grade shows that the level of the final grade can be well predicted by the test battery. In psychological literature validities of R = .60 or higher are said to be highly satisfactory, especially for the conditions of a selection system already in use. It is somewhat surprising that even the result in the simulator check, which is conducted after 34 months of training and about 40 months after the psychological selection, can be predicted with a multiple correlation of R = .61 by the selection test battery.

REFERENCES

Eißfeldt, H. and Maschke, P. (1990). Bewährungskontrolle eines psychologischen Auswahlverfahrens für den Flugverkehrskontrolldienst anhand von Kriterien der Berufsausbildung. Hamburg: DLR Report DLR-FB-316-90.

EUROCONTROL (1988). *Survey - Selection and recruitment of controllers.* Luxembourg: EUROCONTROL Doc. No. 88.10.17.

Goeters, K.-M., Steininger, K., Adam, N., Fichtbauer, S., Kruse, H., and Maschke, P. (1987). *Eignungsauswahl für den gehobenen Flugverkehrskontroll und Flugdatenbearbeitungsdienst. Entwicklungsstand und Kontrolle des Verfahrens.* Hamburg: DFVLR-IB 316-87-01.

Rock, D., Dailey, J., Ozur, H., Boone, J., and Pickrel, E. (1981). *Selection of applicants for the air traffic controller occupation.* Washington, DC: FAA Report No. FAA-AM-82-11.

Steininger, K., Goeters, K.-M., Fichtbauer, S., Adam, N., and Nordhausen, M. (1983). *Eignungsauswah von Bewerbern für den Flugverkehrskontrolldienst: Konzepte, Methoden, Ergebnisse.* Hamburg: DFVLR-IB 316-83-02.

5

Progress in computer-aided testing
Gernot Schuhfried

In the past few years the trend towards computer-aided assessment has clearly intensified. This is not surprising in view of the fact that computer-aided assessment offers a multitude of advantages:

- Maximum objectivity in testing due to the use of algorithms that are fully reconstructable and can be repeated at any time;
- Maximum standardization of testing conditions;
- Optimized instruction of test subjects based on the principles of programmed teaching;
- More diagnostic information within a shorter time through flexible test strategies;
- Automatic recording of elements of behaviour that could not be registered systematically in a traditional testing environment, e.g. response times, solution strategies, tension or stress reduction strategies;
- Reduced social stress for the test subject through individual testing without direct control by the test administrator or other testees;
- Improved test economy through automation of all standardized procedures such as instruction, test presentation, evaluation and in some cases interpretation;
- Presentation of a variety of testing procedures on a single testing unit; Possibility of constructing complex experimental configurations that are not feasible with conventional methods;
- Markedly improved acceptance of the testing procedure by the test subject, if not always by the psychologist.

Of course, I also wish to mention the objections that are being raised against computer-aided diagnostics. Some critics have warned that computer technology will lead to an impoverished diagnostic environment, with rigid and inhuman procedures and no room left for intuition. Booth (1988) on the other hand feels that the reasons underlying such apprehensions may simply be insufficient familiarity with the technology and, apart from that, the latent fear on the part of psychologists that they might be replaced by the computer or at least lose some of their influence in the diagnostic process.

Home or personal computers are designed for games, word processing and accounting, and in these applications exhibit a surprisingly good price/performance ratio. As soon as the user departs from these areas, however, serious malfunctions may occur. There are many examples in the literature illustrating that profound technical knowledge is necessary to construct experimental configurations that are free from artefacts.

Standard computers show a number of hardware limitations when used for psychological applications:

- Response time of the computer, depending on a number of factors, e.g. clock frequency, type of hard disk, quantity of data stored on it;
- Excessively slow reaction time of the system with no exact time definition when presenting graphics;
- Keyboard unsuitable as reaction medium;
- Lack of simple input media such as keys, control knobs, joysticks or lightpens;
- Flickering of the display;
- Insufficient screen resolution;
- Time measurement with resolution below 1/20 sec is problematical;
- Stimulus display limited by technical capacity of the screen;
- No possibility of collecting analogue data.

Naturally, some of these weaknesses may be insignificant in a specific application. The obvious solution is to use a common computer as a basic unit and to expand it with special cards to obtain the hardware properties required. I should now like to present such a commercial concept, which in fact was the first to be developed along these lines (Figure 1). To date, more than 350 of these systems are in use. This equipment has become something of a standard.

The central unit is a standard IBM/IBM-compatible computer. All messages relevant to the test administrator are displayed on the monitor. One slot of the computer contains an additional board with its own highly efficient microcomputer system including a graphics processor, analogue inputs, speech synthesizer, timers, lightpen logic and interfaces for external psychological testing devices.

The test subject works on an absolutely flicker-free high-resolution screen. The lightpen enables the subject to make very direct responses through 'pointing'. It is possible to create virtual keypads.

Apart from the lightpen the test subject uses a panel to enter his responses. Input of analogue data with control knobs and joysticks is an important feature.

An interface is available controlling psychological peripheral units such as a tachistoscope or reaction timer.

The combination of two processor systems offers a very high processing capacity. Thus it is possible to run a test and to read and process physiological data by means of the physiological unit in the background at the same time. A further development based on this concept is the ART90 PC/S.

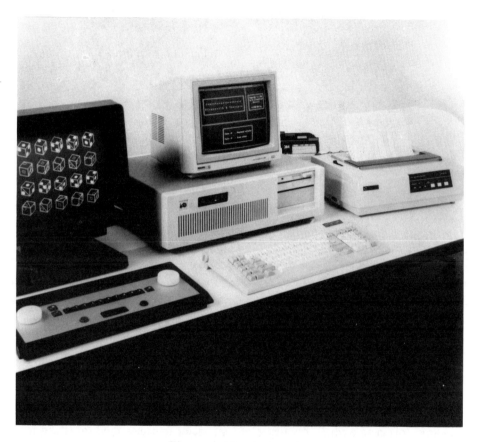

Figure 1. The test system

I show only the best subject station (Figure 2). In the middle is the subject's monitor. Above is the screen of the tachistoscope. The device on the right is the Determination Unit, measuring accuracy of reactions to multiple stimuli. The unit to the left of the screen is the reaction timer. The leftmost device is used to test cognitive functions. The rows of lamps form the peripheral perception unit.

Figure 2. Subject station

Such equipment is practically a complete psychotechnical laboratory that can be used for many different purposes.

Now a few comments on the system program: the program used for these applications is MS-DOS, which must be adapted to the specific requirements by means of operating system extensions.

The presentation of testing and training programs is controlled by a test guidance program, which by virtue of its special features facilitates the test administrator's job substantially. The individual test procedures consist of three parts: instruction, actual test presentation, and computation and interpretation of results as required. For procedures using testing devices, carefully elaborated instruction programs are essential to achieve test economy.

The procedures are designed increasingly in accordance with programmed teaching principles. This guarantees that only subjects who actually know what they are expected to do reach the test phase proper. The test program presents the single items and records the subject's reactions. Usually a solution vector showing the time needed to complete the items is generated and stored. The evaluation program accesses these data and computes the raw scores. Then test scores are compared against norms automatically.

At present there are available more then fifty testing programs, including:
 – questionnaires, e.g. the 16PF or MMPI, and testing programs such as:
 – Memory;
 – Alertness;
 – Long-term attention;
 – Spatial orientation;
 – Cognitive functions;
 – Perception;
 – Motor performance;
 – Sensorimotor ability with one or more secondary tasks;
 – Speed and accuracy of reaction, particularly under stress.

An important point is that efficient statistics programs such as SPSS can access and process the stored data directly, which facilitates the establishment of a data base for standardization, validation, and other diagnostic research projects.

With respect to future objectives, one important point is certainly the design of new test procedures that make full use of computer support. During the past few years more advances have been made in the field of adaptive testing. The difficulty with this kind of test is that a large pool of one-dimensional items is required with a known degree of difficulty.

This takes me to the next point: computer-supported item design based on models such as the linear logistic test model by Fischer or the linear exponential model by Scheiblechner. These models, which are often difficult to handle, permit an explanation or prediction of item difficulty. In certain cases a theory of item construction may even be developed. Where this is possible, and provided that the tasks involved can be defined for computer application, such items can be generated by the computer. This allows the generation of many items with predetermined qualities and facilitates the creation of a large item pool as it is required in adaptive testing. Ideally, items are customized for each test subject while the test is running, which enables attaining the desired solution probability of 50%.

It is possible even now continuously to improve and optimize existing tests. Data on type of reaction and reaction times are gathered routinely from all test subjects and the most valid and most powerful items can be identified. Ongoing data collection and processing enable continuous updating of tests and norms.

Computer-aided testing certainly does raise some ethical problems. In past years, guidelines have been worked out by the American Psychological Association and the BDP Testing Board that are designed to protect both test subjects and psychologists from potential abuses of computer-aided testing.

6

The Defence Mechanism Test and success in flying training

Menno Harsveld

ABSTRACT

The Defence Mechanism Test (DMT), a projective technique to identify a number of information processing styles with negative side effects on the quality of performance, has been administered to flying-training applicants within the Royal Netherlands Air Force. The DMT was used on an operational basis from September 1984 until March 1988, when its use was cancelled on the basis of an evaluative study described here.

The first attempts to assess the predictive validity of the test, at the end of 1984, yielded moderately positive results. However, the results of a second study with larger numbers in October 1986 were rather discouraging.

In the hope that the test would prove valuable when pilot-trainees were followed up over longer periods of time, and to take a closer look at the raw test data in search of single clearly defined predictors among the mass of DMT observations, a third study was conducted. The results, however, were even more disappointing than before.

DMT test scores failed completely to contribute to the prediction of success in flying training, not only when the classic 'Initial Pilot Training' criterion was used, but also when use was made of information on performance in the advanced phases of training. Attempts to find better ways to condense the data into separate scores with well defined conceptual content did not brighten up the picture.

As a by-product of the analysis of raw data, assessments of the reliability of the measurements became available. It became clear that the DMT is an extremely unreliable measuring instrument.

These results were presented at the third DMT conference, held in Vienna in September 1987. In answer to critical remarks some additional research was done, and the various analyses were replicated on greater samples. The results, however, were no more favourable.

INTRODUCTION

The use of projective methods has since the post-war period become less and less popular within military organizations, mainly because of the discouraging results of attempts to establish their value in predicting the future behaviour of testees. The failure of these methods to predict what military organizations want them to predict has been recognized not only by opponents of the psychodynamic orientation in psychology. Many psychologists and psychiatrists regard 'wide band procedures' as instruments that can hardly be missed as adjuncts to questionnaires and other instruments aimed at measuring certain traits and behaviours. It has become rare, however, to encounter psychologists who claim that they can predict course outcomes, war-time psychiatric incidents, or the quality of performance using these techniques. Their utility, as Meehl (1954) has pointed out, seems to lie more in their ability to provide 'hints' or give direction to further enquiries into areas of emotion and concern to a particular subject at a particular time.

The Defence Mechanism Test (DMT), originally developed by Kragh and later adapted by Neuman, a projective technique aimed at detecting the presence of 'dangerous' tendencies to perceive and process information incorrectly, has gained popularity within several military and non-military settings, notwithstanding the above-mentioned state of affairs. The test is characterized by high face validity as far as predicting performance in stressful, complex environments is concerned. It seems obvious that flying an aircraft or managing a complex organization puts high demands on perception and information processing in general. Psychodynamic theory offers a theoretical system of terms describing the way in which people handle threatening information. Although psychodynamic theory is renowned for its resistance to falsification, its basic terminology is attractive, even to opponents of the psychodynamic orientation. Few psychologists refute the notion that some people, especially when under threat, show marked changes in information processing behaviour. Denial of threatening, but obviously present, information, or attempts to 'redefine' information so as to lessen its threatening content, are quite common, or at least seem to be. It is clear that such strategies can be dangerous in situations involving real threats.

Considerations of this kind have undoubtedly contributed to the popularity of the DMT. It is, however, questionable whether this popularity is justified. Relatively few facts have validated its actual usefulness as a predictor of 'dangerous tendencies', and, what is more, there seem to be no grounds to accept the assumption that the DMT actually measures what it purports to measure. It would be difficult to refute the suggestion that the DMT is nothing more than a test in which 'some information containing threat' is presented to a testee, whose responses are then scored using psychodynamic concepts.

Questions regarding the justifiability, reliability, and validity of projective techniques may be looked upon as academic as long as it is not claimed that these techniques, when used, can provide more helpful hints. The DMT, however, has been presented by its developers as being able actually to discriminate between successful and unsuccessful performers (managers, pilots) in stressful environments. That claim, in conjunction with the fact that administration of the test is time and money consuming, justifies a close look at the actual behaviour of the test as a predictor.

This chapter summarizes the outcome of an investigation to find out what use can be made of the DMT in predicting the outcome of pilot training within the Royal Netherlands Air Force. The RNLAF has been using the DMT for more than five years on an experimental basis. A minimal cut-off score on P-NORM, the summarizing measure as calculated following the guidelines specified by Neuman, has been applied to prevent 'restriction of range'. A total of 286 pilot trainees have since the beginning of the project entered initial pilot training. Earlier, preliminary research yielded moderately positive results when pass-fail criteria for initial pilot training were used. Only a few pilot-trainees had at that time progressed to the more advanced courses. Among those who were successful, there seemed to be a weak tendency towards higher scores on P-NORM. Therefore, it was hoped that, by following up trainees over extended periods of training, the DMT would prove to have hidden qualities. Also it was hoped that, by returning to the raw test data and carefully evaluating the contributions of single observations to the prediction of success, a clearer picture of the possible usefulness of the DMT would emerge. Furthermore, a closer analysis of the raw data would make it possible to obtain a global appreciation of the reliabilities of DMT measurements.

METHOD

Data reduction

After administration of the DMT, a large body of data is available. The smallest units are single observations called 'signs'. The detection (by the scorer) of one of the 54 possible signs is a qualitative observation, referring to a specified misinterpretation of stimulus material by the testee.

The standard procedure for administration of the DMT consists of presenting two parallel forms. In turn, each form consists of a maximum of 22 stimulus exposures, i.e. tachistoscopic presentations of the picture, with exposure time increasing in a stepwise manner from .005 seconds to 2 seconds. Subjects respond to each exposure with a short verbal report (sometimes prompted by the test leader) and with a drawing. As a result, initial scoring produces two parallel lists of signs, each consisting of a maximum of 22 shorter lists, representing the signs that were detected by the scorer in the response to a particular exposure.

This body of qualitative information had to be reduced to arrive at some sort of summarizing report on the behaviour of the testee. The prescribed method is a complex one, involving categorization of signs into 10 main groups, a weighted quantification of information into several 'aspects', the use of several tables based in part upon previously gathered validation data, and the computation of a final summarizing measure, P-NORM. In the process, consideration is given to the number of times and in which of the two 'percept-geneses' a given sign is detected, and also to whether signs are detected early or later in the percept-genesis. The prescribed method of data reduction contains, on closer inspection, many elements that justify questions as to their rationale. Leaving these questions unanswered for the time being, we decided to follow several lines in order to arrive at data to be used as variables in our research.

Firstly, we decided to use P-NORM as a candidate predictor of success in flying-training. P-NORM is claimed to represent a scale having interval properties. Its value ranges from 1 to 9, 1 representing an overall high level of defence. Testing the difference between the mean P-NORM of groups of successful and unsuccessful trainees should with regard to these claims be a simple but appropriate way of validating the DMT 'as scored according to the rules'.

Secondly, we devised methods to distil other candidate predictors from the raw data in ways that would by-pass some of the more questionable elements in the prescribed data reduction procedure. We decided to return to the raw data (detections of signs), to leave the original categorization scheme (of 54 possible signs into ten main categories) intact, but to apply no further reduction and/or transformation to the data than summing detections of exposures within 'holons' (phases in the percept-genesis of a subject). What we arrived at were counts of occurrences of each of ten 'main forms of perceptual defence'. Summing took place within each of three holons: early, middle, and late. Since the test is administered twice in parallel forms, referred to as percept-geneses 1 and 2, the reduced data becoming available can schematically be described as follows: a count of occurrences for each (of two) percept-geneses, for each (of three) holons, and for each (of ten) main defence mechanisms.

Thus for each subject a total of 60 (2 x 3 x 10) measurements became available. To this we added (again for each of two percept-geneses and for each of three holons) a count of the number of different mechanisms applied by the subject and also a specification of holon-length, an indication of the number of exposures needed by the subject to reach certain criteria of 'conclusiveness'. This added 12 (2 x 3 x 2) measurements for each subject, resulting in a total number of 72 measurements available for each subject. Given the limited numbers of subjects available for study, it was clear that further reductions were necessary.

For reliability analysis, it was decided to sum over holons within percept-geneses to arrive at ten summarizing counts for each of the two parallel test administrations. This made it possible to arrive at global comparisons between behaviour in the two test series for each of the ten main groups of defence mechanisms.

For analysis of external validity, it was decided to sum over holons also, keeping in mind that separate comparisons for holons would always be possible for exploratory purposes. In fact, looking at early, midway, and late holons did not turn out to show a markedly different picture, i.e. summing over holons did not appear to hide important aspects of the data.

Finally, it was decided for purposes of clarity to apply two separate methods of handling the count data. The first involved recoding these data into simple all-or-none statements, expressing whether a certain mechanism was applied at all by the subject; the second kept the count data intact, recognizing the possible relevance of their quantitative nature and making it possible to apply statistical analysis at rank-order or interval-scale level. By applying both methods, it became possible to analyse two aspects of the data. Firstly, the reliability of the measurements could be assessed according to a simple and straightforward method, by determining whether people who apply a certain mechanism (one or more times) in percept-genesis 1 tend to do the same (one or more times) in percept-genesis 2. Cross-tables and the computation of Chi-square statistics suffice to answer that question for each of the ten main defence mechanisms.

Secondly, by correlating the count data between the two percept-geneses, another form of reliability assessment became possible, taking into account the degree to which a subject applied a certain mechanism.

External validity could also be assessed with respect to both discrete (all-or-none) and continuous measures. Firstly, comparisons (again using cross-tabulation and Chi-square statistics) could be made between successful and unsuccessful trainees, with regard to whether they applied a certain mechanism one or more times or not at all. Secondly, the degree to which successful trainees apply a certain mechanism could be compared with the degree to which the unsuccessful do the same, using non-parametric comparison methods.

RESULTS

Global description of the data

Table 1 contains a global description of the data. The entries show, for each main group of defence mechanisms, the following measures.

- *Incidence in PG1:* the percentage of testees (N = 823) applying a given mechanism (one or more times) in percept-genesis 1. The complement of this percentage indicates the proportion of testees not at all applying the mechanism;
- *Incidence in PG2:* the corresponding measure for percept-genesis 2;

Degree in PG1: the mean number of times a given mechanism was
applied by the testees. This figure is based upon the mean of the
original count data summed over holons;
Degree in PG2: the corresponding measure for percept-genesis 2.

Table 1. Incidence among testees and degree of application of
10 defence mechanisms (N = 823)

Mechanism	Incidence		Degree	
	PG1	PG2	PG1	PG2
Regression	8%	12%	2	3
Repression	42%	52%	3	3
Isolation	97%	96%	9	10
Denial	10%	9%	2	2
Reaction-Formation	57%	26%	3	3
Aggressor Identification	2%	3%	2	2
Auto-Aggression	31%	21%	2	2
Opposite-Sex Identification	82%	50%	5	4
Introjection	83%	46%	7	4
Projection	22%	13%	3	4

These figures allow some immediate conclusions to be drawn. Firstly, the
two forms of the DMT as administered by us do not seem to function as
parallel tests. The incidence of some mechanisms appears to be higher
among testees in PG1. The largest differences are those for reaction-
formation, opposite-sex identification, and introjection.

Secondly, within percept-geneses, there seem to be large differences
between mechanisms with regard to their incidence among testees. Some
mechanisms are quite common, others are rare. The figures for isolation
show that virtually no-one fails to misinterpret the stimulus material in this
particular way. The same applies, to a lesser extent, to opposite-sex
identification and introjection. These findings, and the finding that some
mechanisms seem to appear predominantly in PG1, strongly suggest that at
least some forms of misinterpretations are common stimulus-effects, i.e.
that they spring not so much from tendencies specific to individuals as from
properties specific to the stimulus material. This situation would largely
invalidate the concept of the DMT. It would not preclude the possibility that
such things as tendencies to defend oneself against information actually
exist, but it would imply that DMT measurements do not point to such
tendencies. As was stated before, there seems to be no a priori justification
for the assumption that administration of the DMT functions as an
'experimental analogy' to putting a person under threat.

It is also known that presenting people with ambiguous information forces them to make several inferences in reaching conclusions. Errors in that process could be caused by specific tendencies to misinterpret information in certain ways, but also by specific common pitfalls in the stimuli themselves. The values in Table 1 suggest that at least some defence mechanisms arise from the latter.

Reliability of all-or-none measures

As was stated in the Method section, reliability assessment was conducted with regard to two aspects of the data. Simple cross-tabulation and Chi-square statistics were used to investigate whether testees who apply certain mechanisms in PG1 have a tendency to do so again in PG2. If such is not the case, no further research is necessary. In other words, a (statistically significant) tendency to repeat certain behaviour in parallel forms of a test must be regarded as a condition *sine qua non* for further investigations into its usefulness as a predictor. The results of this analysis are shown in Table 2.

The values can be explained as follows. Ideally one would hope that all persons displaying a certain behaviour trait in PG1 would do so again in PG2. A certain amount of measurement error would be accepted, but at the very least a statistically significant trend towards repetition would be required. The Chi-square statistics as reported in the table have been computed from 2 x 2 cross-tables, representing behaviour in PG1 (application of a mechanism one or more times or not at all) cross-tabulated with behaviour in PG2. When Chi-square is high (associated type I error probability below .05), there is support for the assumption that the probability of applying a certain mechanism in one form of the test is statistically related to the probability of doing so in the parallel form. For the entries under SIG in the table, a + sign denotes significance (type I error probability less than .05) and no entry denotes no significance.

As can be seen, eight mechanisms pass the minimum test. For the other two mechanisms, we must conclude that information on their application in one form of the test does not give any information on the probability of application in the parallel form. This lends further support to the suggestion in the previous section that the behaviours in question are largely elicited by specific properties of the stimulus material, or, in other words, that they are not tied to personality.

For the eight mechanisms passing the minimum test, some further questions with regard to their reliability remain to be answered. As yet no attention has been given to the strength of the (significant) associations found. The use of measures for purposes of prediction requires more than minimal reliability. One way of getting an indication of the strength of the associations that were found is to examine the cross-tabulations themselves.

Table 2. Tendency to repeat behaviour
over percept geneses (N = 823)

Mechanism	Chi^2	Sig.
Regression	70.34	*
Repression	16.28	*
Isolation	0.00	
Denial	47.53	*
Reaction-Formation	33.72	*
Aggressor Identification	1.43	
Auto-Aggression	38.16	*
Opposite-Sex Identification	20.94	*
Introjection	12.59	*
Projection	62.03	*

* = statistically significant

For regression, the incidence among testees in PG2 was 12%. Looking at those persons who applied regression in PG1, we see that among them the incidence of regression in PG2 was 44%. This is a significant rise in probability above the 'a priori value' of 12% (see Table 2). However, the figure is far from impressive. From the fact that someone applies regression in PG1, it cannot be concluded that there is a high probability that he or she will do so again in PG2. As we will see later, we can also state that regression seems to be partly related to stable factors. Such a partial relationship can be very interesting in exploratory research. Typically, however, when use has to be made of test scores as predictors, stronger associations are required. For instance, reliability coefficients below .70, although indicating highly significant variation due to factors tied to the testees, are normally considered too low. Significance means only that the hypothesis of 'no association at all' is an improbable one. Table 3 specifies, for those mechanisms passing the minimal test for reliability, the expected and observed incidences in PG2 among testees applying the corresponding mechanism in PG1.

Keeping in mind that 'expected' here means the incidence that would be expected if behaviour in PG1 and PG2 were unrelated, significant indications of relationships are clearly visible in this presentation of the data. Those who apply one of the mechanisms in PG1 are more likely than others to do so again in PG2. But we also see that the associations found are very weak when evaluated against the standards of test reliability. Knowing that someone applied a certain mechanism in PG1 leaves us, in most cases, fairly uncertain as to what can be expected in PG2. At the very best (in the case of regression) the a priori probability can be raised from 12% to 44%. For the other mechanisms, only small revisions are justified by the data.

Table 3. Expected and observed incidences of mechanisms
in PG2 amongst PG1 appliers (N = 823)

Mechanism	Expected	Observed
Regression	12%	44%
Repression	52%	61%
Denial	9%	30%
Reaction-Formation	26%	34%
Auto-Aggression	21%	35%
Opposite-Sex Identification	50%	54%
Introjection	46%	49%
Projection	13%	31%

Reliability of the continuous measure

Recoding the data on an all-or-none basis may have obscured some important results. Subjects applying a mechanism just once are grouped together with those doing so many times. In the prescribed method of condensing the raw scoring data (see Neuman), the number of times a mechanism is applied is heavily weighted. Another, perhaps better, way of assessing the reliability of the measurements might therefore be to leave the count data (see Method section) intact and correlate the PG1 and PG2 count data. Table 4 gives the results of this analysis, using non-parametric (rank order) correlation coefficients.

A picture emerges that is very similar to that found when the qualitative, all-or-none, aspect of the data was investigated. There are very weak associations between the degree to which a mechanism is applied in PG1 and in PG2. All correlation coefficients differ significantly from zero. Thus, by taking into account a broader aspect of the data, it can be shown that most measures contain at least some person-specific components. At the same time, however, the size of the correlation coefficients is so far below standard that all mechanisms should be characterized as having poor reliability. This is corroborated by reliability analysis in which the mechanisms in PG1 and PG2 are considered as a 20-item test. The resulting split-half reliability coefficient (0.47) is equally unsatisfactory.

There is another consideration that might invalidate the reliability of obtained DMT measures even further. It is prescribed practice, when scoring PG2 data, to look back at PG1 data when application of certain mechanisms is detected, in order to re-evaluate the scoring. The rationale behind this is that certain signs might have been overlooked while scoring PG1 data. Naturally, as a side-effect of this practice, the correlation between both parallel forms of the test is inflated. There is no clear indication of the extent to which the latter has occurred.

Table 4. Correlations between count-data for PG1
and PG2, respectively (N = 823)

Mechanism	Correlation
Regression	.31
Repression	.16
Isolation	.11
Denial	.26
Reaction-Formation	.24
Aggressor-Identification	.06
Auto-Aggression	.24
Opposite-Sex Identification	.24
Introjection	.18
Projection	.30

To summarize, all measures discussed thus far are characterized by poor reliability. The mechanisms seem to be largely determined by factors outside the personality of the testee, but at least there is substantial support for the thesis that these behaviours also reflect stable behavioural tendencies. However, to indicate what must be understood by 'largely determined by factors outside the personality of the testee', the contribution of 'stable behavioural tendencies' may be estimated as no more than 10%. This figure is based upon the square of the highest correlation between parallel tests that was found (the coefficient for regression).

Finally, the freedom that scorers have to modify PG1 protocols after detecting signs in PG2 may have inflated the reported correlations.

It will be clear that attempts to find evidence for predictive power of the measures described will yield only results that will vanish with cross-validation. Since most of the variance does not seem to be tied to persons, only non-systematic effects can be expected. Nevertheless these measures were kept for further analysis.

Of course, P-NORM, the summary measure as specified by the developers of the test, must also be considered as a candidate. P-NORM remains unaffected by the transformation applied to the data. Its reliability cannot be determined since it is based upon two parallel tests considered as one. There are no a priori arguments to exclude it from analysis.

Two further measures, thus far only briefly mentioned, are candidates for external validation. The first is the mean length of holons, indicating how many exposures the testee needs to reach conclusiveness; the second is the mean number of different mechanisms applied by the testee, a measure that could indicate to some extent the severity of his defence strategies. The former will be referred to as holon length, the latter as mechanism variety.

Validity

The poor reliability of the measures discussed in the previous sections makes investigation of their use as predictors of success in flying training rather academic. Still, we decided to make comparisons between successful and unsuccessful trainees, using them as predictors along with P-NORM, which was derived according to the rules specified by the developers of the test and has thus far an unknown reliability.

Comparisons were made using two criteria. The first, the 'IPT criterion', is dependent upon passing or failing during 'Initial Pilot Training'. Of 286 trainees with DMT protocols, 183 had successfully completed this part of training. The second, the 'pre-operational status criterion' or PSC, is dependent upon whether trainees succeed or fail in attaining pre-operational status. For jet-pilots, this status was considered to have been attained after having passed Euro Nato Joint Jet Pilot Training (ENJJPT, Sheppard Air Force Base, USA). For rotary-wing pilots, pre-operational status is defined as having successfully completed the Helicopter Theatre and Tactical Conversion (HTTC). This course is given after return to the Netherlands from Fort Rucker, USA.

After attaining pre-operational status as defined above, it is rare to fail in any of the subsequent conversion courses. The PSC criterion may thus be considered to be a 'final' one. The available data allowed for the formation of one group of 54 trainees successful on this criterion and one group of 138 unsuccessful. It should be noted that the unsuccessful group includes those trainees who failed during initial pilot training. Conversely, passing the PSC criterion implies having passed the IPT criterion. Thus, these criteria are not independent. Rather, the PSC criterion is based upon following up trainees over an extended period of time. For this same reason, sample sizes are smaller for the PSC criterion. A relatively large proportion of trainees with DMT protocols have not yet completed pre-operational training.

Comparisons were made for two aspects of the data, the all-or-none measure and the continuous measure. However, since the results did not differ, only the most inclusive, continuous, measure will be reported.

For these comparisons non-parametric methods (Mann-Whitney U-test) were used, because of the non-normal nature of the count data distributions. For approximately normally distributed measures, Student's T-tests were also used, but since the results did not differ, the same statistics will be reported for all measures.

Comparisons were made separately for PG1 and PG2 data. Thus 50 simultaneous comparisons were made. Differences are reported as significant if the associated alpha is .05 or less. It must be noted that, using this rather liberal approach for exploratory purposes, two or three significant differences are to be expected on the basis of chance alone, given the number of simultaneous comparisons.

Table 5 shows the results of the comparisons using the IPT criterion. In the columns under PG1 and PG2, the direction of the observed difference and its significance are reported. The direction is reported as 'E(xpected)' or 'U(nexpected)'. Following the rationale behind the DMT, one would expect unsuccessful trainees to score higher on counts of mechanism applications, to use more different kinds of mechanisms, and to need more exposures to reach conclusiveness.

In the table, mechanism variety represents the mean number of mechanisms applied on one exposure and holon length the mean numbers of exposures needed before conclusiveness criteria were met. One would expect unsuccessful trainees to have lower values on P-NORM. Significant differences are marked S, non-significant differences NS (alpha greater than .05).

These results are striking in a number of ways. Firstly, it can be seen that trainees who failed IPT do not apply more mechanisms, do not take longer to reach conclusiveness, and do not score lower on P-NORM. Further, only in the case of regression in PG2 does the difference reach the specified significance level in the expected direction. With regard to two other mechanisms in PG2 (denial and auto-aggression), the difference is significant but in the unexpected direction. Thus, our findings do not justify any statements that would challenge the hypothesis of 'no differences between populations'.

PSC criterion

Table 6 shows the results of comparisons using the pre-operational status criterion. For this criterion, none of the differences reaches significance, so these data are also in concordance with the 'no differences' hypothesis.

DISCUSSION

Measuring instruments aimed at identifying traits or behavioural tendencies linked to personality have a poor reputation for predicting future behaviour in applied settings. This applies even to instruments with established reliability and a solid foundation in psychological theory, and also for projective techniques. The DMT seems to lack reliability first of all.

This is not meant to deny the existence of behavioural tendencies to deny or distort information in pathological ways. There seems to be no evidence, however, that the DMT detects such tendencies. The results of this

Table 5. IPT comparisons per mechanism (N = 823)

Mechanism	Sign/Dir'n PG1	Sign/Dir'n PG2
Regression	NS	S(E)
Repression	NS	NS
Isolation	NS	NS
Denial	NS	S (U)
Reaction-Formation	NS	NS
Aggressor-Identification	NS	NS
Auto-Aggression	NS	S (U)
Opposite-Sex Identification	NS	NS
Introjection	NS	NS
Projection	NS	NS
Mechanism-Variety	NS	
Holon-Length	NS	NS
P-NORM	NS	

Table 6. Comparisons using the PSC criterion (N = 192)

Mechanism	Sign/Dir'n PG1	Sign/Dir'n PG2
Regression	NS	NS
Repression	NS	NS
Isolation	NS	NS
Denial	NS	NS
Reaction-Formation	NS	NS
Aggressor-Identification	NS	NS
Auto-Aggression	NS	NS
Opposite-Sex Identification	NS	NS
Introjection	NS	NS
Projection	NS	NS
Mechanism-Variety	NS	NS
Holon-Length	NS	NS
P-NORM	NS	NS

investigation even suggest that phenomena detected by the DMT are to an extremely large extent unrelated to any stable tendencies at all.

The rationale behind the DMT is that some people defend themselves against threatening information by denying or distorting it. It is not unreasonable to suggest that, by forcing people to reconstruct information on the basis of minimal cues (as presented by short exposure times), the tendencies one is looking for could be revealed. In the case of the DMT, however, one might wonder how and why testees should consider themselves in any way threatened by the information presented to them.

Furthermore, apart from the question of whether DMT material causes conscious or subconscious feelings of being threatened, it is clear that presentation of ambiguous information may result in many 'errors of perception' with no relation to personality. The results of this investigation even suggested that some 'errors' (isolation, introjection) are common ways of interpreting the presented information. Other errors are less common but seem to appear and disappear from the behaviour of subjects in more or less random fashion.

One may argue, as was actually done in Vienna at the third DMT conference in 1987, that the methods used to condense data have done damage to significant, deeper aspects of the data. That should, however, have resulted in P-NORM predicting the criteria better than the derived methods, but this was clearly not the case. Nevertheless, it was decided to repeat the validity analyses using 'intact' predictors. For this purpose we took the variables Neuman uses to compute so-called 'U-values' and from which he derives his ten aspects and P-NORM. These variables comprise different combinations of signs and are quantified and weighted on the basis of their frequencies and the percept-genesis(es) in which they occur.

The results of these analyses yield a picture very similar to the one presented before with regard to the condensed data. In the case of the IPT criterion, eight out of 62 (there are 31 variables per PG) differences were significant, five of them in the unexpected direction. As for the PSC criterion, nine differences were significant, six of them in the unexpected direction.

Finally, the ten aspects according to Neuman were used themselves as predictors, as a replication of earlier studies based upon smaller samples. Again, the results look very similar. As for the IPT criterion, three out of ten aspects showed significant differences between successful and unsuccessful trainees, two in the unexpected direction. In the case of the PSC criterion, there is one significant difference, which is in the expected direction.

To conclude, the most simple explanation for the reported findings would be that people undergoing the DMT perform a large number of non-systematic misinterpretations of the material and a small number of systematic ones. These seem to form no reliable basis for the prediction of the results of flying training.

REFERENCES

Kragh, U. (1960). Defense Mechanism Test: A new method for diagnosis and personnel selection. *Journal of Applied Psychology,* 44, 303-309.

Kragh, U. and Smith, G.W.J. (1970). *Percept-Genetic Analysis.* Lund: Gleerups.

Kragh, U. (1969). *Manual of the DMT.* Stockholm: Skandinaviska Testforlaget.

Meehl, P.E. (1954). *Clinical Versus Statistical Prediction.* Minneapolis: University of Minnesota Press.

Neuman, T. (1978). *Dimensioning and validation of defense mechanisms in percept genesis: A hierarchical analysis of pilots' behaviour under stress.* Stockholm: FOA Report C 55020 - H6.

7

Training mental rotation skills

Diane L. Damos

ABSTRACT

This paper presents the results of three experiments examining the training and transfer of mental rotation skills. The purpose of these experiments was to determine if individuals could improve their mental rotation skills with practice and if mental rotation skills were generalizable. All three experiments demonstrated that the speed of mental rotation improved dramatically with practice. Mental rotation skills were found to be generalizable although transfer tended to decrease as the training and transfer stimuli became less similar.

INTRODUCTION

Background

Recently, 'situational awareness' has become a topic of much interest. Although this term has no generally accepted definition, it usually means the pilot's awareness of his entire state. This includes the position of the aircraft relative to the ground, the location of other aircraft, and the operational state of the aircraft and its systems. During the last few years, several investigations have attempted to find ways to improve the pilot's situational awareness. Almost all of these efforts have attempted to improve situational awareness by adding new displays to the cockpit or changing the information presented to the pilot. The research reported here involves training as another approach to increasing situational awareness.

A major aspect of situational awareness concerns the pilot's knowledge of the position of other aircraft relative to his aircraft. Such knowledge involves skills in visualizing the position of an aircraft from different attitudes, in remembering the position of several objects in three-dimensional space, and in extrapolating the position of aircraft that the pilot cannot see. Although pilots clearly learn skills related to visualization, little research has been conducted examining these skills.

The purpose of the experiments reported in this paper was to determine if one of the skills important to visualization, mental rotation, could be

67

improved through extensive training. A second purpose was to determine if the mental rotation skills developed using one stimulus would transfer to another. If mental rotation skills are stimulus specific, then developing a training programme for these skills will be difficult.

The three experiments reported here represent a first step towards developing a training paradigm for situational awareness. Because these studies are a first step, they deal only with picture plane (two-dimensional) rotation. A fourth study dealing with mental rotation in the presence of a concurrent task has just been completed and will be reported elsewhere.

General approach

To study mental rotation, the paradigm developed by Cooper and Shepard (1973) was used. The subject's task was to distinguish as quickly as possible between a standard stimulus and its mirror image. Stimuli were presented at the upright (0 degree) position and at the 60, 120, 180, 240, and 300 degree positions. A trial consisted of 30 presentations of a stimulus and 30 presentations of its mirror image. The stimulus and its mirror image were presented five times at each orientation. Three stimuli were used in these experiments: F, G, and a 24-point abstract shape (stimulus #29, Vanderplas and Garvin, 1959). Subjects used the index finger of their dominant hand to make a 'standard' response and the index finger of their non-dominant hand to make a 'mirror' response.

Because one of the purposes of this experiment was to study the effect of extensive practice on performance, the experiments required ten sessions and were conducted on normal working days on two consecutive weeks. Subjects performed one experimental session per day. Subjects in the experimental conditions performed the mental rotation task with one stimulus during the first week and with the second stimulus during the second week. Subjects in the control conditions used only the second stimulus and performed for one week only. On each day of the experiment the subject performed 36 trials. Thus, subjects in the experimental conditions made 21600 responses; those in the control groups made 10800 responses.

All subjects were males between the ages of 18 and 35. None had any flight training. In all three of the experiments, each of the groups contained 10 subjects.

In the first experiment half the subjects performed during the first week with the letter 'F' and transferred during the second week to the letter 'G' The other half of the subjects began with the letter G and transferred to F. Experiment 2 had three groups of subjects. One group performed the first week of the experiment with the letter F and transferred to an abstract shape. The second group began with the letter G and transferred to the same abstract shape. The third group, the control group, performed only with the abstract shape. Experiment 3 had two groups of subjects. The first began with the letter G and transferred to the abstract shape. The second group, the control, performed only with the abstract shape. Unlike all of the preceding conditions, the experimental group of Experiment 3 practised using increments of rotation of 36 degrees rather than 60 degrees. That is, stimuli were presented at 0, 36, 72, 108, 144, 180, 216, 252, 288, and 324 degrees. Thus, for this group, both the stimulus and the orientation changed between the training and the transfer condition.

RESULTS

Extensive research has revealed that subjects mentally rotate the stimulus to the upright position and then determine if the stimulus is the standard or mirror version. In the vast majority of experimental conditions the subjects rotate the stimulus as if it were a physical object. That is, subjects rotate the object through all the intervening orientations before reaching upright. Thus, if the stimulus were displayed upside down, the subject would rotate it through 180 degrees before bringing the object upright. Because subjects rotate the stimulus in the manner described, the relation between correct reaction time and the absolute degrees of rotation can be described as

$$RT = a + bD \qquad\qquad\qquad 1)$$

where
    RT is the correct reaction time;
    a and b are parameters to be fitted;
    D is the absolute degrees of rotation from upright.

In Equation 1, the 'b' parameter, which is called beta, is the slope of the function relating correct reaction time to the degrees of rotation. Thus, this parameter reflects the rate at which the individual can mentally rotate the stimulus. The 'a' parameter, which is called alpha, represents several information processing stages, including the encoding of the stimulus, comparison, and response selection.

Effects of extensive practice
Several recent experiments (e.g. Schneider and Shiffrin, 1977) have demonstrated that the Sternberg task (Sternberg, 1969) becomes automatic with practice. That is, the number of items held in memory no longer affects reaction time. The mental rotation task is similar in many respects to the Sternberg task. Consequently, practice might have a similar effect on performance: correct reaction times might not be represented by Equation 1 after practice. That is, the effect of rotation angle might disappear.

To test the effects of extensive practice, the last nine trials of each week in all three experiments were selected for examination. An analysis of variance with angle of rotation as one factor was conducted on the correct reaction times. If the task became automated with practice, the subject would not have rotated the image to the upright position. Therefore, no main effect of angle of rotation should be found in the analysis of variance. In all cases the 'standard' and 'mirror' responses were analysed separately. Only in Experiment 1 was the effect of rotation non-significant. This lack of significance occurred for both Weeks 1 and 2. Thus, in Experiment 1 it appeared that with extensive practice either the subjects' processing was fundamentally altered or the rate of rotation became so great as to be mathematically indistinguishable from infinity. The implications of this result are, however, diminished by the failure to replicate the finding in the subsequent experiments.

Transfer of training
In 1985, Spears demonstrated a new method of determining transfer of training using curve fitting. A detailed description of this method is impossible because of space limitations. Briefly, however, the transfer data are fitted using some equation. Spears's method then identifies transfer by interpreting the parameters of the equation fitted to the data. For the types of equations used to fit performance data, at least three, and usually four, parameters may reflect transfer. The first is called the initial level and represents performance on the transfer task unconfounded with the learning that occurs on the first trial of the transfer task. The second parameter is the rate of performance improvement on the transfer task (the learning rate). The third parameter represents the asymptotic level of performance (the level of performance after an infinite amount of practice).

In all three experiments the variables of primary interest were the 'a' and 'b' parameters of Equation 1. For each experiment each experimental day was divided into two sessions, each week thus containing ten sessions. For each session estimates of 'a' and 'b' were obtained for each subject for correct 'standard' responses and correct 'mirror' responses. An average for each session for 'a' and for 'b' was then obtained for each group in the experiment by averaging the individual subject values. Again, separate averages were obtained for standard and mirror responses.

These averages were then fitted using the equation:

$$DV = p_1\, e^{(p_2 t)} + p_3 \hspace{4cm} 2)$$

where
    DV = the 'a' or 'b' parameter of Equation 1;
    $p_1 + p_3$ = the beginning level;
    p_2 = the rate of learning;
    p_3 = the asymptotic level of performance;
    t = the session number.

This equation was used because it resulted in good fits to the data. No theoretical guidelines were used in its selection.

Again, the results of the three experiments are too extensive to be discussed in detail. Instead, a brief summary of each experiment will be given. In all cases no a priori reason existed to assume that transfer would be found for any of the three parameters of Equation 2. If it did occur, however, it would most likely affect initial performance and then gradually decrease; traditionally, transfer benefits tend to diminish with practice. Thus, if transfer occurred, it would probably affect the beginning level of performance, which was represented by the sum of p_1 and p_3.

The results of Experiment 1 showed significant positive transfer for both groups for both the 'a' and the 'b' parameter. Positive transfer occurred for both standard and mirror responses and usually involved differences in the beginning level of performance and the learning rate. Thus, prior practice with a letter provided better initial performance and resulted in faster learning during the transfer phase of the experiment. Surprisingly, in a few instances prior training appeared to result in better estimated asymptotic performance on the transfer task.

The analyses from Experiment 2 showed less transfer than Experiment 1. Analyses performed on the 'b' parameter (the rate of rotation) showed no positive transfer. Thus, learning to rotate a letter had no effect on the speed of rotation of an abstract shape. The analyses performed on the 'a' parameter (the intercept) did show positive transfer but only for 'standard' responses. Subjects who had trained with a letter had faster initial 'a' values than the control subjects. Experimental subjects also had faster estimated asymptotic values of 'a'. These results, when considered together, indicate first that prior training with one type of stimulus does not improve the rate at which another type of stimulus is rotated. Some improvements in performance do occur, but these may be caused by the subject's familiarity with the response keyboard and may not reflect any benefits in information processing caused by prior training.

Interestingly, the results from Experiment 3 were very different from those of Experiment 2 even though Experiment 3 used the same stimuli and was methodologically similar. Prior practice with a letter did not benefit the 'a' parameter of the transfer task. Prior practice did, however, affect the initial rate at which a subject could rotate the abstract figure and resulted in a faster estimated asymptotic rate of rotation.

DISCUSSION

This series of three experiments had two primary purposes. The first was to determine the effect of extensive practice on mental rotation skills. The second was to determine if mental rotation skills would transfer from one task to another. All three experiments examined the effect of extensive practice on performance. The three experiments as a series examined the limits of the generalizability of mental rotation skills by decreasing the similarity of the stimuli and the procedures between the training and the transfer task across the experiments.

Only Experiment 1 demonstrated that, with extensive practice, the rate of mental rotation was mathematically indistinguishable from infinity. Although this finding was not replicated in the following two experiments, all of the subjects obtained rotation rates between 2000 and 5000 degrees/second. Such rates appear to be sufficient for all practical purposes.

Transfer of training was measured using a curve-fitting technique suggested by Spears (1985). Equation 2 was used to fit both the 'a' and 'b' parameters of Equation 1. In Experiment 1, significant transfer was found between training with one letter and transferring to another letter for both the 'a' and the 'b' parameters. Prior practice affected both the initial levels of 'a' and 'b' and their estimated asymptotes. The benefit of prior practice on early transfer performance is a common finding. The effect of prior practice on the estimated asymptotes is difficult to explain; there is no reason to believe that a limited (although extensive) amount of practice with one stimulus should 'permanently' affect performance with another stimulus. Currently, no explanation for such effects can be given.

Experiments 2 and 3 generally showed less transfer than Experiment 1. Again, these results were anticipated; the training and transfer stimuli were very similar in Experiment 1 and very different in Experiments 2 and 3. Although transfer was found in Experiments 2 and 3, the locus of the effect was not the same in both studies. In Experiment 2 transfer was found for the 'a' parameter, which reflects the encoding, comparison, and response selection stages of information processing. In Experiment 3, transfer was found for 'b', the rate of mental rotation. Although the differences between these two experiments are difficult to explain, the fact the transfer occurred in both studies is encouraging. The fact that transfer occurred for the 'b' parameter in Experiment 3 is especially encouraging; this parameter is of primary interest for increasing the spatial information processing skills of pilots.

Admittedly, these results are of limited usefulness in developing a training programme for pilots to improve their spatial information processing skills. They do, however, indicate that such a programme may be possible. The next steps in developing such a programme are to examine mental rotation skills for three-dimensional rotation and for situations where more than one object is present.

ACKNOWLEDGEMENT

This research was supported under Contract #N00014-86-K-0119 from the US Naval Medical Research and Development Command. Capt. Tom Jones was the contract monitor. The author thanks Mr Eric Grose, Mr Qing Wan, Mr A. Kumar, Mr C. Bhat, and Ms Katie Cole for their help in collecting and analysing the data.

REFERENCES

Cooper, L., and Shepard, R. (1973). Chronometric studies of the rotation of mental images. In W. Chase (Ed.), *Visual Information Processing*. 75-176. New York: Academic Press.

Schneider, W., and Shiffrin, R. (1977). Controlled and automatic human information processing: I. Detection, search, and attention. *Psychological Review*, 84, 1-66.

Spears, W. (1985). Measurement of learning and transfer through curve fitting. *Human Factors*, 27, 251-266.

Sternberg, S. (1969). The discovery of processing stages: Extensions of Donders' method. *Acta Psychologica*, 30, 276-315.

Vanderplas, J., and Garvin, E. (1959). The association value of random shapes. *Journal of Experimental Psychology*, 57, 147-154.

8

Psychological testing in aviation:
An overview
Paul Kline

In this discussion I want to make a few observations about psychological testing for the selection of personnel from the viewpoint of psychometrics rather than from the viewpoint of the consumer, in the hope that this different perspective may be valuable.

The first point that is sometimes forgotten among the demands of the job is the psychometric model underlying our testing procedures. It is an assumption that has been made most explicit in the work of Cattell and his colleagues (e.g. Cattell, 1981), namely that performance in any job is a function of four groups of factors: ability, personality, motivation, and mood. Psychometric assessment batteries should contain, therefore, tests of all these variables which are both reliable and valid. That is why it is surprising to learn that interviews are so widely used. In a few hands interviews can be good but whose hands these are is difficult to establish.

There is a second assumption in the model as it is used in selection. This is, of course, that for each specific job optimal weights for these variables can be found empirically and these should be used in selection procedures.

Most of the chapters in this section have essentially been concerned with this second issue, the validation of the selection battery. Nevertheless there are many problems with the application of the psychometric model and I shall discuss the most important of these briefly and indicate how they bear on practical work.

The first concerns the choice of variables to be used in the selection procedure. As I have argued there are four relatively separate categories. In practice the fourth category of moods or states is rarely used. This is because, by definition, they vary from occasion to occasion, so that any one measurement is likely to be not unreliable but variable. This fluctuation, note, is not unreliability, but measurement error. Actually mood could be important in many contexts where vigilance was important. However, without repeated measurement the assessment of moods and states is unlikely to be valid and it is probably best to write the problem off as measurement error.

The second problem is more severe. This concerns the choice of variables and tests; if truly adequate job and task analyses exist, the choice of variables is made easier but it must be based on a priori reasoning, unless there is much previous empirical work which indicates what variables are involved. It is useful to analyse the meaning of a priori. What it really means is that we have used some theory, implicit or explicit, to choose the variables. In this case it is reasonable to ask how good our theories of aviation performance, or come to that performance in any job, really are. I think that it can be seen that there is a lot of guesswork in the work we do. Of course, it may be objected that there is so much known about the good pilot and the good navigator that we know what to assess. This, however, cannot be so in an imperfect world, where there are training failures, accidents, and indifferent performance, even among highly selected personnel.

One possibility to improve the selection of variables, especially in the initial development of selection batteries, is to bear in mind two criteria. One is the previous work in related occupations, where clearly the highest weighted variables are the ones to choose. The second is the factor analytic delineation of the field. Thus the most recent work in the field of abilities shows that there are five second order ability factors, embracing a considerable proportion of the variance, and around 20 smaller first orders (Carroll, 1981). Similarly in the field of personality, Kline and Barrett (1984) showed that four second-order factors regularly emerged but that most of the primaries were unreliable and resulted from poor rotations. In general it is fair to say that the field of personality is not well served by tests. There is a vast number of psychometric personality tests but most are flawed by poor factor analytic construction or by poor reliability. The EPQ is difficult to impugn but it is so general because its three factors are so broad that its use as a discriminator for particular occupations rather than broad categories of jobs must be limited.

In the field of motivation there is a real problem. I think it is fair to say that this is the field of testing that is the least well developed, especially factor analytically. I stress factor analysis because there is a severe problem with tests that are not factorially pure, even if they appear to yield useful results. This arises from the simple fact that identical scores are not necessarily psychologically equivalent since their factorial composition may be different. In the motivational sphere the only factored tests are those of Cattell, the Motivational Analysis Test and its High School version. However, there is considerable doubt concerning the validity of these measures (Cooper & Kline, 1982). The Jackson range of tests, such as the Personality Research Form (Jackson, 1967), is well constructed but is based upon a personality theory of unproven validity, that of Murray (1938), and has little evidence of validity as distinct from reliability. This is why the Defence Mechanism Test (Kragh, 1985) is so appealing, but I shall discuss that test later. Suffice it to say, at this point, that measurement of motivation is a real problem.

Within all these fields of measurement, ability, personality, and motivation, there is a further common difficulty that I shall simply mention. Even if we have decided what variable to use there is the question of what test. Here the only guides should be suitability as regards length and difficulty, and reliability and validity. This latter is best gauged by factor loadings. We should use only tests which load highly on their relevant factor. This is all so obvious as to be hardly worth saying. Yet it is frequently overlooked both in applied and theoretical psychology.

I shall now discuss some further problems with personality and motivational tests which must be faced by those in the business of selection. There is a real difficulty with personality inventories and similar psychometric instruments. If we think honestly about the richness of personality and then read through the items of typical psychological tests, there is a gross disparity. Unless we had a profound faith in the methods of psychometrics and experimental psychology, it does not seem possible that this is all there is to personality: the content, for example, of the EPQ. There must be something missing. Do you enjoy parties, do you feel nervous, do you like talking, are you easily put off? There is not a lot more in that test. This is not just my personal idiosyncrasy. Alice Heim, many years ago now (Heim & Watts, 1966), complained of the insult to the intelligence offered by many forced-choice items enquiring, for example, as to whether you would prefer to visit a bank, a sewage works, or a meat factory, with no space for none.

Attempts to overcome these obvious deficiencies have not been wholly successful but I shall discuss two of the more promising, objectively scored and analysed, projective tests and the Defence Mechanism Test, about which I have decidedly mixed, but I hope not confused, feelings.

First to projective tests. Projective tests are supposed to reveal an individual's deepest layers of personality, his unconscious conflicts and complexes. They have a broadly dynamic and psychoanalytic orientation. As such they cannot be accused, as were questionnaires, of having a simplistic approach to personality. Unfortunately, however, it is extremely difficult to demonstrate that they have much validity and most of them are not reliable. By the standards of orthodox psychometrics they are poor tests, as even an advocate of them, such as Semeonoff (1976) would agree. Certainly, in their standard form, they could not be recommended for practical application.

However, it is possible to score projective tests objectively, as Holley (1973) demonstrated with the Rorschach, a method that can be applied to any test and even interviews. In essence the projective test response is subjected to a detailed content analysis, 1 if a feature is present, 0 if absent. These scores can then be subjected to statistical analysis.

Some examples will clarify the method. In the House-Tree-Person Test subjects are asked to draw each of these things. In objective scoring, if a subject draws a huge billow of smoke then huge billow of smoke (bigger than 5 cm) could be a variable on which he scores 1. Other subjects who drew this would also score 1, the rest 0. In this way reliable scoring for projective tests is possible. These data can then be subjected to any appropriate statistical analysis. For example, in a study of criminals Hampson and Kline (1977) carried out a Q factor analysis, creating groups of offenders and non-offenders. The variables contributing to this discrimination can then be examined. Holley (1973) used the Rorschach in this way to discriminate between schizophrenics, depressives, and controls. However, Q analysis is not the only possible statistic. Chi-squares can be used to examine the differences in response between groups, and there are many other possibilities. Full details may be found in Holley (1973). In my view there is not enough research into the validity of these procedures in the applied setting, although this must be done before the method could be advocated with confidence.

The Defence Mechanism Test (Kragh, 1985) is a highly interesting instrument, developed in Scandinavia by Smith and Kragh as part of the experimental study of unconscious processes in personality, all subsumed under the name of percept genetics (Kragh & Smith, 1970). In a paper of this length I cannot describe the theoretical background to this test. Suffice it to say that it involves the subliminal presentation of a threatening stimulus at gradually increasing degrees of brightness. The sequence of descriptions and drawings of the stimulus through the series is said to reveal defences, in the psychoanalytic sense – repression, reaction-formation and the like. Its relevance to aviation psychology is high since it is claimed in the handbook to the test (Kragh, 1985) that it is powerful in the selection of jet-pilots (in several air forces), where it eliminates those who have accidents, and attack divers. It is assumed that it is equally valuable for all occupations where sudden stress and danger are involved. The theoretical rationale is simple: those who defend will pay less attention to the threat and thus be involved in accidents.

Nevertheless there are problems with this test, as Harsveld noted. The fact is that it has low reliability, as I also have found in a recent as yet unpublished study. Furthermore there is not good evidence for the validity of the test. As I pointed out (Kline, 1987) the scoring system makes just the same assumptions in labelling responses as defences as do analysts in labelling their patients' responses, the differences being that DMT data are public; anyone can inspect what subjects have written and drawn.

Cooper and Kline (1986) carried out an empirical study of the DMT where it was related to a number of other tests, including the 16PF. Certainly it did not simply measure extraversion or neuroticism. In this study the test, which was not administered as the standard DMT but through a projector and shutter, showed some evidence for validity. It was factored and the first general factor did correlate with success on an RAF jet-pilots' course.

An interesting thing about this factor was that it was obtained from an objective analysis of the DMT, as described above for projective tests. This factor was replicated in a student sample where it was related to a perceptual defence measure. This study supported the notion that perhaps what is measured by the DMT is perceptual defence and that this is a measure of repression. What is clear, however, is that the standard scoring procedures, in the hands of most psychologists, are not valid or useful. Much more research work is required for the DMT before it could be used in selection with any confidence.

From this section, it can be concluded that the selection of aviation personnel is proceeding along rational and sensible lines and is reasonably successful. What, however, is required, is some new and powerful technique, if the predictions are to be improved. Attractive as the DMT is, it is not yet ready to meet this need.

REFERENCES

Carroll, J. (1981). Individual differences in cognitive abilities. *Paper at NATO Conference.* Kingston, Canada.

Cattell, R.B. (1981). *Personality and Learning Theory.* New York: Springer.

Cooper, C. and Kline, P. (1982). The internal structure of the Motivation Analysis Test. *British Journal of Educational Psychology,* 52, 228-233.

Cooper, C. and Kline, P. (1986). An evaluation of the Defence Mechanism Test. *British Journal of Psychology,* 77, 19-31.

Hampson, S. and Kline, P. (1977). Personality dimensions differentiating certain groups of abnormal offenders from non-offenders. *British Journal of Criminology,* 17, 310-331.

Heim, A.W. and Watts, K.P. (1966). The Brook Reaction Test of Interests. *British Journal of Psychology,* 57, 178-185.

Holley, J.W. (1973). Rorschach analysis. In P. Kline (Ed.), *New Approaches in Psychological Measurement.* London: Wiley.

Jackson, D.N. (1967). *Personality Research Form.* New York: Research Psychologists Press.

Kline, P. (1987). The scientific status of the DMT. *British Journal of Medical Psychology,* 60, 53-9.

Kline, P. and Barrett, P. (1983). The factors in personality questionnaires among normal subjects. *Advances in Behaviour Research Therapy,* 5, 141-202.

Kragh, V. (1985). *The Defence Mechanism Test.* Stockholm: Persona.

Kragh, V. and Smith, G.W. (Eds.) (1970). *Percept Genetic Analysis.* Lund: Gleerups.

Murray, H.A. (1938). *Explorations in Personality.* New York: Oxford.

Semeonoff, B. (1976). *Projective Tests.* London: Wiley.

Part II

Simulation

9

Introduction to simulation
John Rolfe

It is only right that a volume on aviation psychology should include a section on simulation. There are a number of reasons to justify this assertion.

Firstly, simulation is established as an essential tool for both research and training within aviation. Secondly, the role of simulation in both civilian and military training is increasing. In commercial aviation, training to acquire, maintain, and assess capability is conducted in flight simulators, with demonstrable benefits in terms of training and cost-effectiveness. For the military, striving to maintain operational readiness with high-technology weapons systems, yet facing increasing constraints from a society growing more attentive to the environment, it is becoming more apparent that the military aeroplane in peacetime can be used only as a part-task trainer. Consequently, simulation is, at times, the only possible method of achieving the required training. Moreover, as the demand grows to train, exercise, and evaluate whole operational groups, the facility to provide networks of training systems becomes more attractive. For a recent review of these topics the reader is referred to the proceedings of the Royal Aeronautical Society's 1989 Spring Convention which had as its theme 'Flight simulation: Assessing the benefits and economics'.

Thirdly, aviation psychology should be directly involved in both training and research using simulators. Two reasons are offered to justify this assertion. Firstly, the keystone to the value of simulation in training is the concept of transfer of training and the need to identify those aspects of simulator fidelity that contribute to effective transfer. Secondly, the evidence is that it is the quality of the elements that constitute the simulation and not just the hardware alone, i.e. the simulator, that determines training effectiveness. This is nowhere more apparent, at least to psychologists, than in the introduction of simulation to command and control training. The recent report by Solick and Lussier (1988) is a most constructive and informative assessment of work in this area. A further challenge that faces psychologists at this time is the extent to which they can persuade training device procurement organizations to consider the use of performance-based rather than the long established equipment-based specifications (Rolfe, 1988).

The chapters in the simulation section of this volume reflect some aspects of the scope of psychological research using simulation. These contributions consider issues involved when using simulation as a selection tool for pilots, as a means of evaluating cockpit display concepts, as a structured and controlled facility for examining pilot decision making, and as a method of simulating communication requirements in a command and control situation. Despite their different themes, identifiable common issues emerge.

Dudfield's chapter on development and evaluation of cockpit display symbology to provide indications of vertical ground features raises the issues of what can be achieved through the use of low-cost simulation in which some features of the real flight environment are absent, and how far it is possible to assume that the results obtained will carry through to low-level flight itself. In this case the problem is recognized and the objectives of the study clearly defined as to obtain information about display symbology and control interactions. The simulator acted as a screening and familiarization device that was acceptable to the aircrew who would be evaluating the refined system in flight.

The contribution by Jorna and Visser gives rise to similar issues but this time in the context of using flight simulation as a tool for pilot selection. Undoubtedly using a flight simulator may make a selection procedure more of a job sample test, but can the simulator be anything more than a sophisticated test of co-ordination and handling skill? Could proficiency in the simulator predict whether the candidate would be capable of adjusting to and accepting the actual flight environment? What these two questions do give rise to is the problem of selecting suitable measures, from those available in the simulator, on which to base predictions of likely success. The authors draw attention to the finding that the instructors making the assessments significantly favoured candidates who scored high on a test of anxiety and whose performance on objective measures of control strategy showed them to be less effective than low anxiety candidates. This finding leads to consideration of the nature of the formal and informal cues used by instructors to assess students and the potential implications of side by side versus tandem seating arrangements in training aircraft.

The chapter by McRae and Pattison also looks at the issue of crew arrangement but in relation to communication and decision making. Their methodology is ingenious; recognizing that to be meaningful any analysis of performance needed to make use of highly skilled performers, they chose a sophisticated computer game as their simulation and students who had already achieved exceptional proficiency on the game (as measured by the game structure) as subjects. The subjects were then paired up to play the game in a two crew configured form. The experimenters report their attempts to analyse the strategies employed and the nature of the communication problems that accompanied critical incidents in the performance of the game.

Two findings emerged from this work. Firstly, an extensive amount of material may need to be recorded and analysed before any examples of communication errors are obtained. To some extent this finding should be accepted as a partial validation that the task employed had relevance to the real world. Cockpit voice recordings are obtained from every flight but only a small number will ever reveal what can go wrong. However, the small number of critical incidents captured by the authors of this paper did reveal similarities with those that have occurred on the flight deck (see McPherson, 1985). The second finding was the difficulty of being able adequately to control the simulation. A computer game, particularly if it is as sophisticated as that used in this study, will offer a range of uncertainties and apparently random occurrences; in this way the interest of the player is maintained and the challenge to go on playing is sustained. However, such a structure does not help the researchers who need to be able to control and relate events in the simulation to anticipated and observed performance. The authors are not alone in using games in this way, and if adequate preparation is undertaken valuable results can be obtained. For example, see Dukes and Matteley (1988) for a report of the use of STARPOWER as a medium for studying the effects of social structure and mobility on attitudes and behaviour; and Norris (1988), who examined the external validity of business games.

The McRae chapter emphasizes the importance of using, wherever possible, simulations that were correctly modelled with the application in mind. A research simulation needs close control over the model, scenarios and measures so that reliable data can be obtained. The chapter by Stokes describes such an attempt: the development of a microcomputer-based simulator for cockpit decision training. The interest and strength of the work, as reported so far, is the extent to which the events represented in the simulation are set out as a branching structure linked by conditional probabilities. Thus the system allows understanding, manipulation, and control, and permits studies of pilot decision making and training to be carried out under repeatable and measurable conditions.

REFERENCES

Dukes, R.L. and Matteley, C. (1988). The effects of social structure and mobility on attitudes and behaviour in a simulated society. *Simulations and Games,* 17, 467-484.

McPherson, M. (1985). *The Black Box: Last Words from the Cockpit.* London: Granada Publishing Limited.

Norris, D.R. (1988). External validity of business games. *Simulations and Games,* 17, 447-459.

Rolfe, J.M. (1988). Training simulation: Knowing what we want and getting what we need. In D. Saunders, A. Coote, and D. Crookall (Eds). *Learning from Experience through Games and Simulations.* Loughborough

Society for the Advancement of Gaming and Simulation in Education and Training (SAGSET).

Solick, R.E. and Lussier, J.W. (1988). *Design of Battle Simulations for Command and Staff Training.* Alexandria VA: Army Research Institute (ARI) Technical Report No. 788.

10

Simulating obstacle avoidance cues for low-level flight
Helen J. Dudfield

ABSTRACT

A 'pilot-in-the-loop' simulation facility using an enhanced graphics workstation to simulate a 3D representation of the real world was developed in order to evaluate a display philosophy for warning aircrew of significant obstructions in their flightpath.

The simulation involved the aircrew flying a Head-Up Display (HUD) that was superimposed onto the 3D background. A plan map presented on a Head-Down Display (HDD) indicated the course that the pilot was to follow. The Mission Controller had artificially placed obstacles around waypoints prior to the trial. The types of obstacles cued included pylons, power cables, radio masts and bridges.

The aircrew flew several missions in a static cockpit simulator. Each mission investigated a different aspect of the obstacle cueing display: symbology design, depth cueing, display clutter, and the possible effects of display inaccuracies on aircrew performance. Both subjective assessments (questionnaire responses) and objective measurements (rms data) were obtained.

The trial results suggested that the proposed display philosophy was a suitable method for cueing obstacles at low level. Future enhancements to the display were identified and discussed.

INTRODUCTION

Situational awareness is an aspect of display design that psychologists have been trying to improve in the cockpit for some time. This paper addresses one specific cockpit display that is intended to enhance a pilot's knowledge of the environment around him, especially during low-level, high-speed flight in the often bewildering environment of a fast-jet cockpit.

One problem that a pilot faces during low-level night or poor visibility flying is the interpretation of sensor information which can warn aircrew of significant obstacles in the intended flightpath. Such obstacles can be defined as anything of significant vertical height, but typically include radio masts, cooling towers, viaducts, power cables and pylons. It is generally found that certain types of obstacles, especially power cables, pylons and masts, have a poor contrast against a typical background. Hence these are often undetected or poorly detected and thus fail to appear on a sensor display, e.g. Forward Looking Infra-Red (FLIR). Additionally, in a two-seater environment the navigator is tasked with selecting a flightpath that avoids obstacles, and can verbally warn the pilot of the known obstructions. The workload involved in this task is greatly increased for the single-seater environment.

In terms of the scenario considered here a display concept was developed that could cue aircrew of dangerous obstacles in their flightpath, hence not only enhancing situational awareness but also, it was hoped, having the by-products of better safety and lower workload. The trial that is described below involved experienced aircrew using an obstacle cueing display in a part-task simulation of a typical flying task.

Obstacle cueing

The ability to display the position of flightpath obstructions has resulted from advancements in onboard navigation systems that can provide the aircrew with accurate position data. One such system, Terrain Referenced Navigation (TRN), uses an onboard data-base to identify the aircraft's position and is independent of the satellite support that other systems need.

The TRN system calculates the height of the local terrain by subtracting radar height from barometric height; these 'spot heights' are then compared to a matrix of heights stored in the onboard terrain data-base. A process of pattern matching continues until a one-to-one correspondence is found between the terrain data-base and the calculated height. The digital data-base can be derived from a number of sources including the world-wide Digital Land Mass Survey (DLMS).

TRN has a number of advantages additional to accurate navigation. It enables aircrew to use a passive navigation system rather than the active Terrain Following Radar (TFR) mode. It could be a versatile tactical information source and provide intelligent ground proximity warning. Furthermore it can enhance the HUD by providing cultural and geographical obstacle cueing.

This chapter describes the latter use of TRN, specifically the development of a display philosophy. The obstacles that were cued on the HUD, enhancing a FLIR sensor, were categorized into several types: cooling towers, industrial complexes, radio masts, pylons and power cables, and viaducts and bridges. These were all cultural cues; geographical information, such as ridgeline enhancement, was not considered. The production of these cues and the simulation facility are discussed below.

Mission objectives

The overall objective of the trial was to examine six aspects of an obstacle cueing display, by 'pilot-in-the-loop' simulation that reflected specific areas of concern. These can be listed as:

- to examine the necessity of terrain masking;
- to assess methods employed for depth cueing;
- to study ways of de-cluttering the display;
- to determine the best means of cueing obstacles;
- to quantify the effect of mismatches between cue and obstacle position;
- to evaluate the effect of display lag on performance.

Simulation facility

The simulation facility was developed to provide a rapidly reconfigurable Man-Machine Interface (MMI) with a particular emphasis on flexibility. The simulator provides a real-time FLIR simulation based on an area around south Wales. This 'real world' also contains vertical obstructions, generated from an obstruction data-base, on top of which computer generated cues can be superimposed (Figure 1). The simulation visuals are generated from an advanced graphics workstation. The aircraft model, system configuration and cockpit interfaces are controlled by a microprocessor.

Simulator hardware

The main hardware components are: a wooden, mock-up cockpit with Hands On Throttle And Stick (HOTAS) controls, a PC, an IRIS 3030 graphics workstation, and a video projection system. Furthermore there is a continuous communication link between the pilot and controller, and a noise simulation of a fast-jet is also produced by interfacing software on the PC with the throttle.

The simulation works through a cycle of events: the cockpit controls are interfaced to the PC, which contains the flight model and feeds aircraft position and attitude data to the graphics workstation; consequently the output from the workstation (the real-world scene) continually changes and is projected onto a large screen in front of the cockpit.

The controller can manipulate several display functions via the keyboard, and the pilot has the ability to perform four tasks by pressing buttons on the control stick. During each run the room is darkened and the controller observes the simulation on a monitor and receives status and trial information.

Software

The generation of the obstacle cueing system involves a series of software steps from the generation of cues to the production of terrain.

Initially the controller created obstacle cues using a symbol editor programme that would allow the generation of line-drawn cues. The controller had the ability to switch between two symbol sets; a third was created to represent the real-world obstructions. The simulation was limited in the sense that the symbols tended to match the obstacle cue shapes accurately and were, typically, visible – this being true for only some sensor images in the real world.

Figure1. Terrain simulation

The next step was to select an area of terrain onto which the obstacles could be positioned. The same area of hilly terrain was used in each mission. The controller defined a mission route by setting up a course of waypoints, and then placed obstacles of different types around the course of waypoints (Figure 2). The waypoints appear as a large cross on the HUD. A specific function joins obstacles that are linked by cables, e.g. pylons.

In advance of running the trial a setup program was created that enabled the independent variable to be declared. This program gives control over all aspects of the simulation and feeds data into the main simulation program.

The information received from the symbol editor, obstruction data-base and setup program specifies the appearance of the simulation. The pilot views a large simulation of a 3D, monochrome-green FLIR scene on top of which a conventional HUD format is presented giving radar height, speed (Knots), attitude and other information (Figure 1). Furthermore the HUD provides the pilot with confirmation of display changes that he has made by pressing stick function buttons.

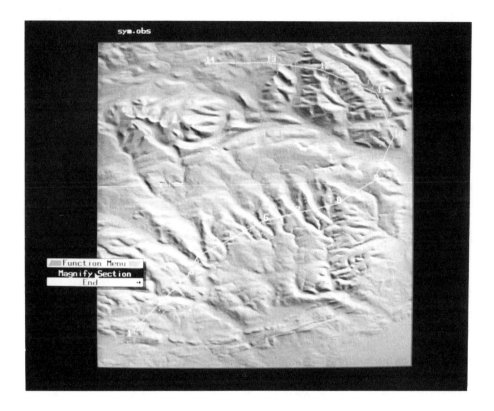

Figure 2. A plan view of the obstruction data-base

The terrain appears as a series of 200m squares which vary in colour and brightness. The sensation of depth is provided not only by the 3D image but also by sun-angle shading. However, there is no textural information. The obstacles are depth-cued by two methods: they become larger and brighter as their range decreases.

METHOD

The simulation facility described was only the means by which the different aspects of the display philosophy were examined. The trial, in total, consisted of three sections: an introduction and initial questionnaire, the completion of six missions in the cockpit simulator, and finally a de-briefing questionnaire.

Subjects
The trial participants were all test pilots with considerable experience of low-level, high-speed, poor visibility/night flying. All were familiar with the concept of obstacle cueing.

Procedure
Prior to the trial each pilot received a briefing booklet that outlined the objectives of the trial and the method by which they would be investigated.

On arrival, the aircrew, having confirmed that they had read the briefing booklet, were given an initial questionnaire to fill in. The information derived from this source gave the experimenter general background information on their flying experience and knowledge of modern avionic equipments and obstruction cueing.

The main block of the trial consisted of the 'pilot-in-the-loop' simulation in which different aspects of the display philosophy were considered. Instructions were given outlining the cockpit controls and trial arrangement, and were supplemented by a practice flight in the cockpit that enabled aircrew to become accustomed to this particular flight model.

Each pilot flew six missions, each having twelve waypoints and approximately equal duration (10 minutes). The controller repeated verbally the mission objectives prior to each run, and was on hand to discuss the cueing philosophy as it was displayed. During each mission rms height error scores were collected and other relevant objective data were stored.

The pilot was finally requested to complete an extensive questionnaire that addressed each aspect of the display philosophy and allowed him to report his overall impressions.

The data analysed comprised responses to the questionnaires, rms height error score, distance at which the cue drift was cancelled, and amount of display lag present when the cue drift was cancelled.

RESULTS

Terrain masking
The first aspect of the display considered was whether terrain should be masked so that obstacles that were partially or completely hidden behind terrain would not be seen. In this first mission the pilot was able to change between screened and unscreened terrain at will.

The conclusion drawn was that masking was an essential component of an obstacle cueing display because (a) it prevented perceptual ambiguity, e.g. the belief that a tower was on top of a hill when in fact it was partially hidden by the hilltop, and (b) it mimicked the real world. The only justification for unmasking terrain was as a tactical aid which could provide a 'look ahead' facility. However, this would probably be limited by the time available for the pilot to look ahead during a low-level mission.

Depth cueing
The ramp of obstacle cue brightness, from the black level to the brightest green, could be set to start at a maximum of 10 km to a minimum of 1 km.

The preferred range to which obstacles should be cued was examined. This was expected to become a compromise between display clutter and a satisfactory supply of obstacle information. In the simulation the pilot was able to switch between four ranges (1, 3, 5, and 10 km) at which obstacles were first cued. The aircrew were typically satisfied with a range of 5 km as providing sufficient situational awareness and minimizing display clutter. However, the optimum range was felt to be dependent on groundspeed.

The minimum distance (1 km) was considered to provide aircrew with a last minute warning of imminent collision, but was found to be too late and too short. When an obstacle was within this range one of three HUD warnings was displayed, the flashing 'PULL UP' being most favoured. The danger of having an attention-getting but annoying pull-up cue was mentioned, a factor that would require consideration during warning system development.

The majority of aircrew found brightness attenuation to be an acceptable method of depth cueing. However, it would be preferable to reduce the brightness of cues relative to that of the HUD symbology to minimize confusion and display clutter.

Display clutter
In addition to de-cluttering the display by range, an algorithm was incorporated into this mission that also thinned obstacles by calculating a zone of priority within which cues were drawn. This zone was based on the range of obstacles and on their bearing in the horizontal and vertical planes.

Four priority levels, representing increasing clutter, were used; the ranges used were the same as before and the bearing angles were relatively acute (less than 10 degrees). The aircrew, who were able to switch between these four priority levels, generally preferred a 5 km range.

Several problems become apparent in the use of this system of priority zones. For example, some obstacles were not cued despite being within the HUD field of view (FOV); cues could 'glint' on and off if an obstacle moved rapidly in and out of a priority zone; and the nature of the algorithm prevented the pilot looking into a turn.

The development of a more interactive, flightpath-predictive, de-clutter facility will provide solutions for many of these problems. Indeed alternative methods of de-clutter, based, for example, purely on obstacle height relative to aircraft height, should be considered.

Cue design

A major purpose of the trial was to develop and evaluate symbology options for cueing obstacles. A limited number of cultural obstructions were cued: pylons, masts, cables, bridges and industrial complexes (Figure 1). Of these, the aircrew were most concerned that pylons, masts and cables be cued because of their poor thermal images. This mission involved a straightforward flight with clusters of the different types of cue positioned around waypoints.

The aircrew were in favour of using symbolic ground-stabilized outlines correlated with the real obstacle's shape, emphasizing the advantage of simplicity. The main cue shape was a triangle for towers and masts; a cross within this shape denoted a pylon (Figure 3). Pylons were connected by cables, and solid features, such as cooling towers and industrial complexes, were cued by boxes.

Cues in the form of outline rather than filled figures were favoured, to maintain visibility of the obstruction that was to be avoided. Aircrew rated the mast and pylon cues as 'quite satisfactory'. However, concern was expressed over the use of the box shape, which was possibly confusable with conventional HUD symbology. Generally it was proposed that a limited number of obstacles should be cued to reduce display clutter and workload.

One of the main advantages of these symbols was that they resembled their counterparts on conventional maps, hence enhancing transfer between displays and reducing unnecessary learning. This was seen as being important for a high workload environment in which individuals can easily revert to previously acquired stereotypic behaviour patterns.

The use of lines between pylons to indicate the presence of power cables was acceptable; indeed it prevented confusions between several towers and a line of pylons (Figure 3). However, it is no doubt important to thin this display element to reduce display clutter when there are several pylon lines. The use of dotted lines to distinguish between multiple pylon lines was also considered acceptable, but the question was asked as to what would happen when there was a multiplicity of pylons. It is suggested that in this case a thinning algorithm would be sensible.

The aircrew were invited to propose alternative ideas about obstacle cues. Most supported the use of conventional map symbology, although some favoured the use of top and bottom cueing in which the body of the obstacle was not obscured. However, separated cues are not as 'perceptually good' in terms of Gestalt principles, and their components may be difficult to match in a cluttered display; there may also be confusion with HUD symbology.

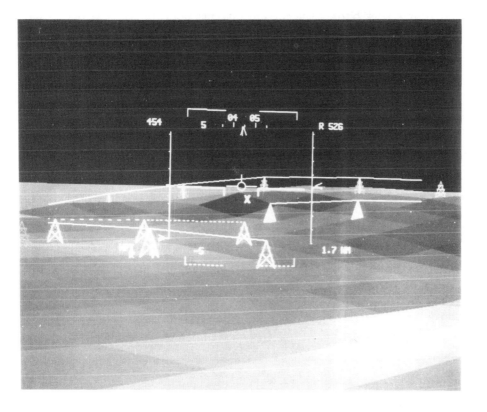

Figure 3. Options for representation of pylons

More general recommendations were that symbology should be as simple as possible. For example, some aircrew questioned the need for the cross within the pylon symbol, since these symbols were connected by cables, and some suggested that a pole could replace the inverted V.

Display inaccuracies
The effect of mismatches between cues and their corresponding real obstructions was considered in this mission. As time progressed the cues drifted away from their obstructions in an east-west direction (Figure 4). The amount of drift could be quantified in metres by measuring the difference between the two display elements. The intention of this mission

was to evaluate the subjective effect of cue drift and to determine the acceptable limit of drift.

Throughout the mission the pilot was able effectively to remove the drift by pressing a stick button; the current distance of drift each time the button was pressed was stored.

Figure 4. An example of display inaccuracy

In most cases aircrew found the cumulative cue drift to be distracting, but their estimates of the effect on the mission varied, probably because the degree of disturbance was dependent on flightpath (e.g. making a turn) and workload. Most aircrew tended to realign the cue and obstacle when they became separate objects. With multiple obstructions, however, cue drift was cancelled more quickly because of the problem of matching several cues and obstructions.

The data indicated that the median distance at which aircrew cancelled cue drift was 56 m, with an average of 17 button presses during the mission profile. A median value was selected for distance because of the presence of 'outliers' attributable to aircrew drifting off the flightpath and hence missing cues.

Although cue drift disturbed the aircrew to differing degrees, it could be concluded that, typically, cue drift greater than 60 m was unacceptable. These results must be considered as applicable only in the simulator environment, in which important elements of the real situation, such as stress, were absent.

Display lag
The inclusion of display lag provided an effective demonstration of how display elements can directly influence user performance. As with cue drift, both objective and subjective measures were obtained. Display lag in this context refers to obstacle cueing, rather than HUD symbology; the delay, relative to real time, in drawing cues on the HUD produces mismatches between cue position and obstacle (Figure 5).

Five levels of lag were considered (1-5 display frames) which ranged between 140 ms and 700 ms. These were compared against the baseline of no lag and against each other. The collection of rms height error scores was central to this mission.

The mission was sub-divided into two sections. Initially lag incremented automatically every 80 frames and could be cancelled by the pilot when it was considered unacceptable. The cancellation facility was removed in the second run and the pilot was forced to fly for a fixed amount of time under each level of lag. The influence of the five levels of lag on flying performance was considered statistically using a one-way analysis of variance (ANOVA).

The results of the ANOVA (Table 1) revealed an extremely significant (p < 0.001) effect of display lag on performance and also illustrated the differing success with which aircrew performed the flying task (p < 0.001).

Table 1. ANOVA summary table

Source	df	SS	MS	F
Lag (L)	5	122104	24420.81	10.94
Subjects (S)	7	123287	17612.50	7.89
L x S	35	78111	2231.75	
Total	47	323502		

Post-hoc comparison of means was conducted using the Newman-Keuls procedure (Table 2). The major finding was that the baseline differed from each other lag level.

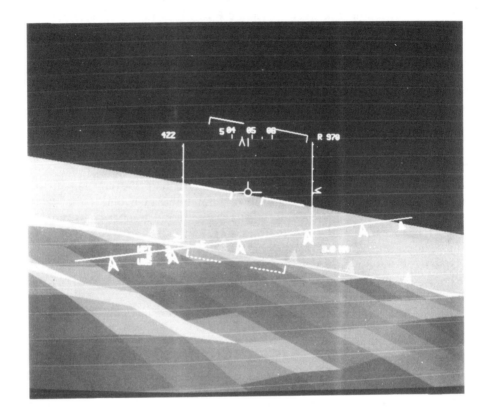

Figure 5. The effect of lag on the display

Aircrew tended to cancel lag after between two and three frames; this matched their subjective reports. The majority reported that display lag affected their flying; although there was considerable variability between subjects, performance decrement increased as a function of lag. The major criteria that pilots reported using for cancelling lag were distraction during manoeuvres, displacement between cue and obstacle, and lack of confidence in cueing accuracy for low-level flight.

The visual appearance of display lag was dependent on the aircraft's manoeuvres. Wings-level flight dramatically reduced the problem of lag; however, difficulty was experienced in a turn, particularly with joined obstructions, and became unacceptable at levels greater than two frames.

Table 2. Comparison of rms error scores for each lag level

Lag level

	0	1	2	3	4	5
0	-	**	**	*	*	**
1	-	-	-	-	-	-
2	-	-	-	-	-	-
3	-	-	-	-	-	*
4	-	-	-	-	-	*
5	-	-	-	-	-	-

$(** = p < 0.01; * = p < 0.05)$

CONCLUSIONS

The six missions highlighted several important design aspects of an obstacle cueing system. The majority of aircrew found the display philosophy to be acceptable but indicated areas of concern: HUD clutter, cue drift, effective de-cluttering, display lag, and the accuracy of obstruction data. The major advantages included reduction of subjective workload, relative ease of interpreting the display, simplicity, and the provision of a sufficient, but not overwhelming, amount of information.

The success of an obstacle cueing system will be dependent on reduction of problems such as cue drift noted above, and enhancement of the acceptable properties of this versatile display.

REFERENCES

Beech, E. (1989). Sight unseen. *Flight International,*   11 February.

Dudfield, H. and Gibson, C. (1989). *The development   of a display philosophy   for an obstacle   cueing   system.* (In press.)

Sweetman, B. and Hewish, M. (1988). Airborne navigation. *International Defense Review,* 1, 35-39.

Whitehead, A., Baggs, F., Jackson, D., and Gibson, C. (1989). *Initial definition   of formats   for a terrain   obstacle   cueing   system.* Unpublished MOD(PE) technical report.

11

Ultra-cheap simulation of cognitive load in a two-man helicopter

A. W. MacRae and S. E. Pattison

ABSTRACT

To investigate the effects of the spatial position of crew in a helicopter we have adapted a commercially available computer game to model the cognitive demands of flight. Although the simulation does not aim to represent helicopter flight realistically, the demands made by our modified game on the players are very similar. Because the game has been available for several years it has been easy to locate a pool of enthusiastic and expert players who closely resemble flight crew in their characteristics and who require no preliminary training. Recordings are made of each game and of the verbal interactions of the players. Analysis of the recordings shows great variability in the patterns of utterances from one session to another and the preliminary data suggest that the most fruitful analysis is going to be of events leading up to the occasional calamities that occur.

INTRODUCTION

Westland Helicopters Ltd. are supporting our research on the possible effects on helicopter aircrew of being in separate cabins rather than sitting side by side as they do in current designs. Questions about the effect of spatial separation of operators also arise in many other situations, such as fixed-wing aircraft, air traffic control, remote conferencing, and the monitoring of highly automated industrial processes. It was not practicable at this stage in our work to monitor live flight or even full-scale simulations. On the other hand, to simulate the major cognitive demands of flight need not require simulation of many of the sensory inputs or physical demands of flight. We decided instead to devise a laboratory task that would be no more than an analogy to flight but aimed to capture as many as possible of the features that we judged to be relevant. Our simulation does not aim to reproduce all the conditions of flight, but abstracts from it those attributes we consider important for our purpose. In particular, we aimed to devise a task with the following features.

- *Co-operation.* We wanted a task in which the participants work to a common purpose, rather than competing or working independently.
- *Concurrency.* We wanted it to require responses to external events in real time, with the participants operating simultaneously rather than taking turns.
- *Need for communication.* We wanted successful performance to depend on the transmission of information in both directions between the participants.
- *Balance of duties.* We wanted a task in which both participants were about equally loaded with responsibilities and duties.
- *Challenge.* We wanted the task to be demanding, requiring skill and a high level of attention.

METHOD

The computer game Elite is available for several types of computer, but the version running on a disk-based BBC machine proved much the best for our purpose. It is a game of space flight and combat, with opportunities for gaining wealth and status by battle and by trading. It uses 3D graphics and gives a strong sense of realism, so that skilled players develop a high level of involvement in its fictional but very detailed universe.

Elite is designed for a single player but we adapted it by showing its video display simultaneously on two screens, each seen by one of the players. One player sees only the top half of his monitor screen, which represents a view through the window of a spaceship. The other player sees only the lower half of his display, representing an instrument panel and a 3D radar view around the ship. The former player (the 'Pilot') sees the local scene (but only in one direction at a time) and flies the ship, while the other (the 'Commander') 'sees' further and in all directions by means of the 3D radar, but has a less detailed local view.

The Commander sits at the computer keyboard and operates all the available functions other than the flight controls and laser weapons. That gives him responsibility for 'hyperspace jumps', arming and firing of missiles, data-base interrogation (to select a course), and selection of direction of view (usually at the request of the Pilot). He also monitors all the instruments and must warn the Pilot about any potentially dangerous conditions, such as overheating or loss of energy for defences. The computer also generates various auditory signals; most are mainly for dramatic effect but some give useful information, such as warnings or an indication that a missile has locked onto a target.

The Pilot flies the ship using a control panel carrying a joystick to control pitch and roll and a rotary knob that controls speed and can also be pressed to fire a 'laser cannon' in combat. Apart from the viewscreen, the only other input he receives is an instrument reading of current speed, plus the auditory signals he hears from the Commander's console by way of the Commander's microphone.

The players wear headsets and converse with each other through them. In this way, the verbal component of their communications has the same medium irrespective of the spatial arrangement of the two players, their displays, and their controls. For example, there is no acoustic reason to speak more loudly or more distinctly when they are apart than when they are together.

To maximize any difference that might be brought about by different spatial arrangements, we have concentrated on comparisons of the same pairs of players, where one player is consistently the Pilot and the other is consistently the Commander and where they are located either side by side or in different rooms. All pairs have the same mission: they are to cross a galaxy from one specified star to another, making a series of 'hyperspace jumps' from star to star by any route they please. Their task is to do so in minimum clock time, and if their vessel is destroyed they must start again.

Each hyperspace jump is of limited distance and can be made only after time has been spent in 'normal space', locating the local star and flying close to it to collect an adequate supply of hydrogen fuel. This manoeuvre requires the Pilot to fly close enough to the star to collect fuel but not so close that the cabin overheats. At all times, the crew is liable to be attacked by pirates, in which case it can fight or sometimes flee. The ship is armed with 'laser cannon', fired by the Pilot, and 'missiles', fired by the Commander. The supply of missiles is limited and they are ineffective against some adversaries. The likelihood of attack depends on the social system and level of development of the star system to which they jump. Frequent attacks delay their mission even though they are likely to survive them, so it is advantageous to select a route through peaceful regions. Long range and short range maps, and detailed information about individual star systems, can be obtained by interrogating a data-base.

We monitor the progress of the game and the verbal interactions of the players by recording the screen display on video cassette and by recording the speech of each player on a separate audio channel to let us analyse the interactions that take place. Having separate audio channels makes explicit which of the players has spoken. Because each player sees only half of the information on the monitor, they must communicate continuously in order to fly.

By means of notices around the University campus we have located a pool of almost twenty expert players. Elite allows players to progress through several grades of skill by accumulating scores from one occasion to the next, and awards promotions whenever a threshold score is reached. All our applicants had reached one of the top three grades and we accepted everyone who applied. It happens that they are all young men, intelligent, skilled, competitive and with high self-esteem. In order to reach the highest grades of attainment in Elite they must have hundreds of hours of practice and we believe that they provide a good analogue to skilled aircrew. There is no problem of maintaining motivation and interest. All have reached a level of skill where there is little real challenge in playing the solo game, and yet they enjoy exercising their expertise. Consequently, they are delighted to have the opportunity to play our new variant, with its somewhat different demands, and where each pair is in implicit competition with other pairs. Sessions are nominally for an hour but players often prefer to continue for longer. The very modest cash incentive we offer is scarcely needed.

RESULTS

The first focus of our study was the pattern of speech communication between the players. When players are together, each can see what the other is doing and can also see what information he is receiving. There is also the possibility of non-verbal communication such as gestures. These sources of information are removed when the players are separated. If they are important, they might produce different patterns of interaction in the remaining channels of communication. We arranged that all the pairs would play twice with the game set up in one room and twice with the players in two separate rooms in a BAAB-ABBA design.

We developed a taxonomy of the various types of utterance that occurred, such as commands, acknowledgements and questions. Analysis is not yet complete, but it is already clear that even when we consider the same pair of players throughout, variation from one session to another of the same kind is much greater than any consistent effects of spatial layout. Thus there is no evidence of any dramatic effect on the pattern of vocalizations.

We have now begun to focus on what happens when things go wrong – most dramatically in the situations when the craft is destroyed – and there are indications that the failures that occur may be influenced by spatial layout. We can study the antecedents by tracing backward through the sequence leading up to the event and also by asking the players to give a commentary on the taped record. Although this phase of investigation has just begun, we have identified one incident in which the calamity was the result of one player paying attention to his partner's display to the neglect of his own, on which a remote threat had developed into a fatal one while he attended to hazards that were properly the responsibility of his partner. Calamitous events are fairly rare with our expert players, but they bear such an obvious relationship to accidents that their detailed study is almost bound to prove illuminating. If necessary, we can increase the difficulty of the task by altering the initial conditions or armaments so as to make misadventures more likely. In fact we think it may be desirable to do so in any case in our next series of studies with these players to maintain a high level of novelty and interest in the game.

DISCUSSION

There are limits to what can be learned from a restricted simulation such as ours. If we were to find that the spatial layout in our game has no effect on performance, we could not safely conclude that it will not matter in flight. Layout might make a difference because of factors that are not represented in our simulation. Thus we can never prove that a variable does not matter in practice: it may not have been given an opportunity to act. Nor can we prove that a variable does matter. Perhaps in our simulation the absence of cues that are available in flight forces players to use information channels that would not be their preferred choice, and perhaps only these non-preferred channels are affected by layout, so that if a full range of information were provided the effect would disappear.

For example, all information in Elite is presented on a VDU screen with only occasional and minor acoustic embellishments. Indeed, the crew learn of a dangerous rise in cabin temperature only by means of the VDU display. Also, we have forced the crew to exchange information continuously, by displaying each source of information to only one of the players. We did that because of our interest in communication patterns but it is not a desirable scheme for practical use.

On the other hand, it should be recognized that even the most elaborate simulation is only a partial representation of reality. It cannot be assumed that any simulation is satisfactory for training purposes until it has been validated by showing how it transfers to the real task; and when a simulation is used for research, to discover something new, there is no prior way of validating its results. The problem is logically the same, and different only in degree, whether we consider our simple system or a full flight simulator.

All simulation results should be viewed with caution, perhaps being treated as no more than indications of which factors deserve detailed study. But the cost of the simulation should be appropriate to the degree of specificity in the questions to which answers are sought and to the precision of knowledge about which aspects of reality need to be represented in the simulation. We believe that our extremely cheap simulation, costing at the very most £1000 in all, is capable of yielding insights that may be useful in guiding, and thus in economizing on, research on live flight or in more realistic simulators whose running costs might exceed the cost of our system every day.

ACKNOWLEDGEMENT

We gratefully acknowledge the support for our research by Westland Helicopters Ltd., in the form of a Research Studentship to S. Pattison and a Research Contract to A. MacRae.

12

MIDIS - A microcomputer flight decision simulator

Alan F. Stokes

ABSTRACT

Jensen (1982) points out that 80-85% of civil aircraft accidents can be attributed to 'pilot error' and that 50% of accidents are the result of faulty pilot judgement. He writes 'In spite of the statistics, attempts to teach [judgement] are almost non-existent... good pilot judgement is learned by the lucky and the cautious over many years of varied flying experiences'. Until recently little was known about flight decision making, except that pilots do indeed make better decisions after explicit pilot-judgement training courses (Buch & Diehl, 1984).

With this in mind, a microcomputer-based simulator for cockpit decision training and research, 'MIDIS', has been developed based on the instrumentation of the Beech C23 (Sundowner), a single-engined fixed-gear aircraft. The formal structure of MIDIS software is that of a 'graph traverser', in which the nodes of a branching structure are linked by transitional probabilities. Each node is a realistic in-flight situation. The system is thus capable of considerable flexibility and is able to simulate the chain of deteriorating circumstances which typifies the development of mishaps in complex time-critical decision-making contexts.

The MIDIS system is configured to permit testing/training under differing conditions of workload and stress, and to date four experimental studies funded by the United States Air Force have been undertaken: a validation study of an information processing model of pilot judgement, a study of expert and novice judgement in IFR flight, and two studies of pilot decision making under stress.

INTRODUCTION

For decades the importance of one aspect of pilot competence, decision making, was neglected. The increased attention now being paid to decision making is timely, however, since rapid development of automation in the cockpit has further emphasized the pilot's role as flight and systems manager, over that of 'stick and rudder' co-ordinator. The airlines are tackling the problem with training programmes that emphasize 'Cockpit Resource Management' (CRM): team work in decision making. This is paralleled by the situation management training in extremely sophisticated flight simulators. The USAF has focused particular attention upon emergency decision making and has introduced training approaches such as Boldface – the regular paper-and-pencil testing of memorized emergency procedures – and Situational Emergency Training (SET) in which students must react to emergency situations devised by reference to F-15 accident reports.

Understandably, these airline and military training programmes are rooted in pragmatic rather than theoretical considerations, and require considerable resources. Hence there is relatively little 'spin-off' for aviation in general or addition to the knowledge base in the field of human decision making. There is a need for a broader programme of research into the cognitive aspects of decision making on the flight deck (Wiener & Nagel, 1988). Therefore the objectives of the work reported here have been twofold:

1. to provide a low cost decision-training aid, based on commercially available microcomputers, that complements present general aviation simulator training; and

2. to use this system in research that will throw light upon the nature of human decision making in general and flight decision making in particular.

FLIGHT DECISION MAKING

Although interest in crew decision making has increased with the recognition of the importance of CRM, published research on individual decision making in the flight environment remains relatively sparse. Work such as that reported by Saleh, Thomas and Boylan (1979) and Hopf-Weichel, Lucaccini, Saleh, & Freedy (1979) has tended to be specific to narrow domains, such as emergency decisions in military situations. This work does not develop a theoretical base that can be generalized to decision making in broader contexts. The same is true of current research in flight decision making conducted within the Artificial Intelligence or 'Expert System' framework. Again, the domain may be specialized, as in air combat manoeuvring decisions (e.g. Goldsmith & Schvaneveldt, 1985). In these approaches the objective tends to be the development of functional simulations or Decision Support systems rather than the development of psychological models or training methodologies. A further body of work on flight decision making has tended to be anecdotal, founded upon intuition-based judgement training programmes or post-hoc analysis of accident and incident reports (e.g. Jensen, 1982; Buch & Diehl, 1984; Giffen & Rockwell, 1987; Simmel & Shelton, 1987; Maher, 1989).

Among other things, this work has highlighted the importance of decision making to aviation safety and the benefits to be gained from explicit formalized decision training. However none of this work has been concerned with the development of a predictive model of flight decision making. Furthermore, with the exception of Maher (1989) none of this work exploits the ideas contained in (non-aviation-related) research on human decision making under risk, carried out by such researchers as Kahneman, Slovic, and Tversky (1983), Slovic, Fischoff, and Lichtenstein (1977), and Einhorn and Hogarth (1981). This body of research contains numerous experiments documenting human biases, heuristics and limitations in decision making and judgement as carried out in a variety of non-aviation contexts; at present, however, it makes only minimal contact with the world of aviation, and as Friedman, Howell, and Jensen (1985) point out, 'it remains to be seen how general these heuristics and biases are and to what extent they degrade performance on actual decision problems' (p. 666). In view of this, the MIDIS system was developed not only as a training device but also as a research vehicle for the investigation of pilot judgement in uncertain high-risk multi-cue decision-making contexts.

SETSCENE AND MIDIS

General structure
The feasibility of a microcomputer-based decision trainer was first explored in a prototype system used as a development tool to define the necessary features of the present operational system. This has been structured in such a way that it can be employed both as a decision-training aid for pilots and as a research tool in the area of pilot judgement. The MIDIS system consists of two programs, SETSCENE and MIDIS, written in PASCAL and running on the IBM AT. Later versions have utilized the on-board voice synthesis capability of the IBM InfoWindow touch-screen CRT.

The first program, SETSCENE, is an editor that facilitates the preparation of 'flights' by the experimenter/flight-instructor. SETSCENE provides input to MIDIS, which controls a text and instrument panel display. The general structure of the MIDIS system places it in a class of programs referred to as 'Graph Traversers' (Doran & Mitchie, 1966). Graph traversers are applicable to situations in which a number of states are connected by a set of transformations or 'operators'. This can be represented as a branching tree-structure graph in which the nodes represent the states and the operators linking them are transitional probabilities.

The states in MIDIS take the form of descriptions of realistic in-flight situations referred to as 'scenarios'. These are similar in concept to the SET scenarios developed at Luke Air Force Base for F15 pilot training, i.e. simulations of real situations requiring decision-making skills (Hopf-Weichel et al, 1979). Unlike SET, however, a MIDIS situation may involve any potential in-flight situation, emergency or otherwise. Each scenario requires that a decision be made among several alternatives presented. The decision influences the occurrence of subsequent scenarios, since it selects the transitional probabilities that will operate. However, the system can be toggled to either 'experimental' or 'training' mode. In the former mode all transitional probabilities are set to 100%, so that the sequence of events is deterministic. As a hypothetical example, every subject who elects to take off with low fuel will find himself having to divert to a distant airfield because of poor weather. In 'training' mode, however, the pilot who elects to take off with low fuel may have a 50% chance of meeting weather below minima at his intended destination. In this mode no two flights need be the same.

A number of considerations influence the scenario sequencing structure that may be used in SETSCENE. First, there is the problem of devising a scenario structure that gives the appearance of being unbounded to the user while in fact having an underlying formal structure that is very constrained. The second consideration concerns the need for this structure to represent the pattern of deteriorating circumstances that often characterizes aircraft mishaps. These misfortunes do not usually occur as a result of one poor decision or one technical malfunction, but rather as a result of several concatenated events opening successive 'gates' to an accident.

Figure 1a represents a structure designed to keep the progress of the simulated flight 'on track', while at each stage allowing digressions into successively less optimal scenarios. (For clarity the figure shows just four branches from any one scenario. In fact there may be up to ten.) This structure is built around 'core' scenarios that represent situations at points along a cross-country flight-track. Core scenarios are to some extent independent of each other, for although they obviously must make chronological sense they do not form a tight causal chain. Other scenarios branching off the core are less favourable to the efficiency or safety of the flight. The less optimal the decision, the more likely that the subsequent scenario will represent a deterioration in the flight. The further down the chain of worsening scenarios the pilot proceeds, the less probable is his return to a core scenario. Ultimately an exit sequence (forced landing, for example) becomes 100% likely. For experimental purposes it is often important that all test subjects have attempted the same number of scenarios, and have gone through identical or at least equivalent flights.

Figure 1b represents a structure that permits a degree of branching while maintaining equivalence. All scenarios in one 'level', the 300 level set, for example, may be instrument failure diagnosis scenarios, although the four strands may represent different routes and heights selected.

Specific features
MIDIS: At present MIDIS has a full, high-fidelity instrument panel based

on that of a Beech C23 Sundowner, the type of aircraft used for training at the University of Illinois Institute of Aviation. This display, implemented via the HALO graphics package and 16-colour Enhanced Graphics Adaptor, represents a full IFR 'blind flying' panel with operating attitude, nav/com and engine instruments. MIDIS accesses SETSCENE files to change the readings on the instrument panel throughout the course of the 'flight' in synchrony with the prevailing scenario. Figure 2 depicts a MIDIS display. Instruments, pointers, flags, and switches have conventional colour coding.

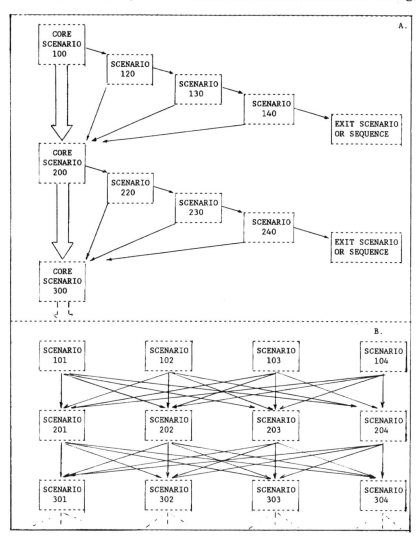

Figure 1. Scenario sequencing strategies in SETSCENE

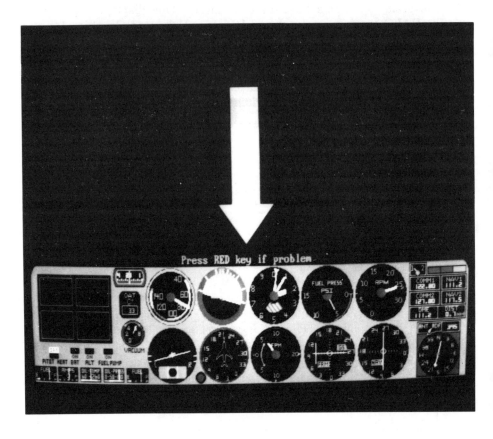

Figure 2. MIDIS instrument panel during a climbing left turn

MIDIS does not attempt to simulate the flight dynamics of an aircraft from control inputs – the province of conventional flight simulators – but it does allow for additional tasks that provide the functional equivalent of cockpit workload. Visual tasks may be presented on a reserved panel to the left of the instrument display (see Figure 2). A joystick-controlled tracking task, for example, could be implemented, or some additional systems monitoring or control task. In the InfoWindow version of MIDIS, synthesized voice can be used to generate 'Air traffic control (ATC) communication' workload.

For our research purposes three abstract secondary tasks have been implemented. These tasks, two visual and one auditory, may be enabled or disabled for any MIDIS run, and, if enabled, may be set to provide a consistent secondary task loading at whatever level is desired.

The first is a Sternberg memory search task (Sternberg, 1975) in which four letters of the alphabet are memorized prior to the flight. Throughout the flight letters are displayed on the reserved panel and the pilot must depress a key indicating whether it was or was not a member of the target set. MIDIS allows the rate of presentation and the permitted response time 'window' to be varied. Errors result in a distracting warbling tone at 72 dBa.

The second visual task is a 'shape cancelling' task in which coloured geometric shapes may appear in any of the four squares on the reserved panel. Each square corresponds to a key on the keyboard. Pressing the correct key removes the geometric shape from the screen before the irritating tone is generated.

The auditory task is also a Sternberg memory search task which involves the presentation of letters via synthesized voice over a headset. As in the visual tasks, presentation rate can be selected as can the maximum permitted response time. Errors or failures to respond result in a synthesized explosion noise and the cockpit voice warning 'ERROR, ERROR, ERROR, ERROR'.

A number of performance variables are monitored, most of them unobtrusively. Four of these relate to response selection: decision choice, optimality, decision time (latency), and decision confidence. Secondary task scores and latencies are also stored. Other variables monitored are problem recognition, problem study time, and reading speed. The pilot's mean reading speed is unobtrusively calculated in syllables per second during the reading of the program run instructions (part of an automatic sequence that includes a system tutorial). Since SETSCENE analyses scenarios and options for word and syllable counts, as described above, individual differences in reading speed are automatically factored out of problem study time and decision latency data.

SETSCENE: SETSCENE permits access to up to ten scenarios from any starting point scenario and up to six decision options per scenario. With each scenario a comprehensive range of instrument panel readings is also stored plus rate of change information. These data are accessed by MIDIS as a subject progresses through a 'flight'. The system can be run without any time limit for responses to problems, permitting, for example, the collection of latency data during experiments. The system can also be run, however, in 'lock-out' mode, which is useful in training. This mode invokes realistic time limits stored with each set of decision options in SETSCENE. An engine failure at take-off, for example, might permit 30 seconds for a decision to be made, whereas a radio-failure problem might be essentially open-ended. If no decision is made within the time allowed, SETSCENE ensures that MIDIS 'locks out' the decision-maker, i.e. defaults to the situation coded as most likely to occur should the pilot fail to intervene.

SETSCENE incorporates two further sets of algorithms: one set is involved in the analysis of text, as outlined above; the other uses Boolean logic to permit any decision or combination of decisions to have a delayed effect upon any subsequent scenario as desired. Take, for example, a case in which the pilot elects to take off late in the day *and* selects the less efficient of two routes *or* chooses to fly a slow economical cruise. This combination of decisions can be made to result much later in, say, arrival by night in poor weather at an airfield with a short narrow runway.

In addition to its 'MIDIS driving' functions, SETSCENE performs a number of important housekeeping operations. As discussed earlier, SETSCENE has a structure capable of modelling event sequences with considerable realism and flexibility. How far this potential is realized, however, still depends heavily upon the quality of the flight information in the data-base.

To date three flights of about one and a half hours' duration have been prepared. Each flight consists of about 40 problem scenarios. SETSCENE has been designed to assist in keeping track of the different scenarios and options in the data-base. Each scenario may be identified according to a set of bibliographic descriptors (such as 'cruise', 'approach', 'weather problem' or 'system malfunction'), and cross-indexed searches can be carried out on these descriptors. This facilitates the construction of new flights as well as the post-hoc analysis of those flights.

For many research purposes a content analysis of each scenario is useful. The system provides for this by permitting a set of content variables to be defined and stored with each problem. For our own research, for example, we performed a content analysis of the situations in terms of their psychological structure. That is, flight-trained psychologists rated each situation as high, medium, low, or zero on attributes such as required mathematical skill, spatial ability, textbook knowledge, and diagnostic reasoning. In this case, then, SETSCENE's search and retrieval capability permits scenarios to be identified or selected on the basis of similar problem structure – a facility important to certain studies of decision making outlined below.

STUDIES USING MIDIS

Our initial MIDIS study was a componential analysis of flight decision making. In this study 38 instrument-rated pilots were divided into two groups, one consisting of those pilots with high flight hours and the other of individuals with fewer than 400 hours. As a convention we adopted the terms 'experts' and 'novices', respectively, for these groups. All 38 subjects were administered a range of domain-independent cognitive tests selected to assess putative information processing components of decision-making ability. These included tests of working memory capacity, logical reasoning ability, spatial ability, visual cue sampling skill, and declarative knowledge of instrument flight regulations and procedures. The subjects subsequently 'flew' an IFR flight from Mountain View, Missouri, to St Louis Regional Airport at Alton using the MIDIS simulator (Wickens, Stokes, Barnett & Davis, 1988).

The results were surprising. We were unable to distinguish between the expert and novice groups on the basis of their decision making. The groups did differ, however, in terms of the problem variables that degraded decision performance, and the individual abilities affecting that performance. Few of the psychometric indices of decision-making components were predictive of decision optimality in novices. Those that were – mainly working memory capacity, spatial abilities, and declarative knowledge – were only moderately predictive. In high-time or 'expert' pilots, information processing measures were hardly predictive at all.

From these results it seems that 'bottom-up' integrative and diagnostic processes in working memory may have a less important role in flight decision making than originally anticipated – especially in expert decision making. More precisely, they may be less important in the option selection stage of decision making.

We have since revised the model of decision making (Stokes, Barnett, & Wickens, 1987) such that it differentiates between cognitive strategies adopted by experts and by novices. Specifically, it posits direct retrieval of domain-specific problem schemata or 'scripts' from long-term memory (LTM) as a distinct alternative mechanism to processes heavily dependent upon working memory. The LTM-related strategy would presumably be more easily available to experts (with appreciable experiential repertoires) than to novices (Figure 3).

This has been investigated in a second individual-differences MIDIS experiment (Barnett, 1989). In this study the performance of 15 expert and 15 novice IFR pilots was contrasted. As in the initial study, all subjects were administered a battery of information processing tests before completing a MIDIS flight. In addition, however, subjects attempted three domain-specific tasks designed to index representations of situational knowledge in LTM. The first, the ATC Recall Task, involved reconstructing both randomized and coherent radio call sequences from memory. We hypothesize that by controlling out memory effects (using recall of the jumbled transmissions) the quality of reconstruction is primarily influenced by the availability of appropriate situational 'scripts' in the pilot's repertoire.

A second task, the ATC Recognition Task, involved building a mental 'picture' of a situation from ATC calls and selecting appropriate diagrams of the scenario. The third task, the Dynamic Diagnosis Task, involved recognition of failures or flight problems (e.g. windshear, suction pump failure, pitot icing) solely by reference to MIDIS instrument panel indications. Subjects subsequently flew a MIDIS flight from Madison, Wisconsin to Mason City, Iowa. The flight, which lasted about an hour and a half, contained 38 problem scenarios.

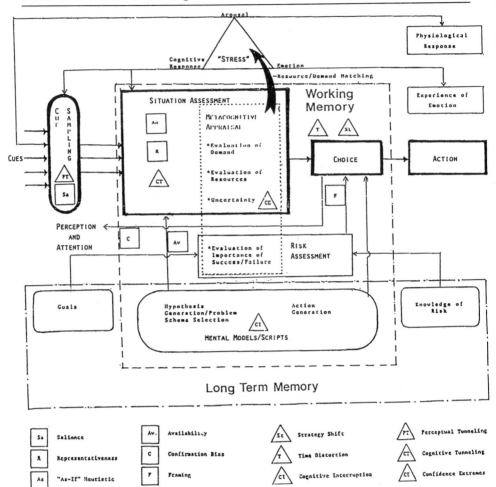

Figure 3. An information processing model of stress and bias in
human decision making (Stokes, Barnett, & Wickens, 1987)

The results showed that the three knowledge representation tests were
indeed better predictors of expert performance than the information
processing tests. Although these findings are consistent with the prediction
of our model, the results for novices are less so: decision performance was
not strongly predicted by the information processing tests. Risk assessment
and logical reasoning tests were significant predictors of novice performance, however, while working memory, visual scanning, and reasoning
tests were significant predictors for experts. Nevertheless, domain-specific
tests were the best predictors of flight decision making in general.

These results certainly reinforce our suspicions that the role of information processing skills is less important than we had originally believed, at least in the option selection stage of decision making. This does not, of course, preclude the possibility that they are indeed significant determinants of earlier processing stages in decision making, such as hypothesis generation.

Stress experiments

In addition to the distinction between information processing and knowledge representational processes in decision making, the model proposed by Stokes et al (1987) has a further significant characteristic – it adopts a cognitive appraisal approach to stress and posits stress/bias synergisms as an important source of error. We hypothesize that 'top-down' strategies utilizing direct retrieval from LTM will be relatively robust in the presence of task-related stress. In contrast, the 'fragile' computational integrative processes in working memory seem likely to be disrupted by stress rather more readily.

In a second set of experiments, then, we examined the effects of stress upon flight decision making. The first study was a between-subjects design (Wickens, Stokes, Barnett, & Hyman, 1987). Twenty novice instrument pilots were pair-matched by flight hours and test battery results. Each subject flew a single MIDIS flight from Saranac, New York to Boston's Logan Airport. One group of ten conducted the flight in a non-stressed condition and the matching group was subjected to stress manipulations during the flight.

Subjects in the stress conditions performed the MIDIS task under four manipulations intended to provoke anxiety: (1) time pressure – subjects were instructed to finish the flight in one hour (the mean time taken by the non-stressed group); (2) dual task loading – subjects were required to perform a secondary task, that is, to respond to visually presented letters on the instrument panel that were stimuli for a Sternberg memory search task; (3) financial risk – subjects were told that their earnings would be depleted for every minute in excess of one hour; (4) irritating noise – failure to perform the loading task rapidly and accurately produced an annoying tone of moderate volume (72 dBa). Loading task errors were also linked to further financial decrement. Even with successful completion of the secondary task, the tone was periodically (and randomly) presented to create uncertainty and doubt over performance.

We were able to demonstrate that significantly poorer flight decision making can be provoked by these manipulations. This deterioration was not, however, found for all problem types. Novice aviators tended to make poorer decisions on problems pre-rated by pilot-psychologists as requiring more retrieval of 'textbook' knowledge from LTM. However, performance on these kinds of problems was not sensitive to the degrading effects of stress (consistent with the predictions of the model). Likewise, novice decisions were also poorer on problems rated high in demand for spatial skills. But performance on these problems was most disrupted by stress, as revealed by a significant stress by spatial demand interaction. This suggests that problems with high demand for spatial operations in working memory were particularly sensitive to the degrading influence of the stress manipulation, again as predicted by the model.

Whether this result was in fact due to a stress-induced reduction in working memory capacity, however, is questionable in the light of a third set of results. These appear to indicate that decision performance was essentially unaffected by the demand for verbal working memory, and this insensitivity was observed equally for stressed and control subjects alike. Working memory is where the clearest stress-related decrements had been anticipated (Hockey, 1986). This result, therefore, is not consistent with the model, but may derive from limitations in the experimental methodology. First, stress effects were inferred from decision performance on problems rated subjectively (albeit by pooled expert ratings). These ratings may have been inaccurate. Alternatively, the decrement in decision performance on spatial problems may have been due, at least in part, to the visual-verbal (screen displayed) nature of the Sternberg task. Since most spatial problems involved instrument scanning, it is possible that these were disrupted more by the need to time-share visually with the Sternberg display than by a reduction in working memory capacity. However, using the SPARTANS battery of aviation-relevant information processing tasks, Stokes and Raby (1989) have shown that similar stress manipulations can be directly associated with significant decrements in performance on working memory and spatial tasks.

Declarative knowledge scores were not significantly different in the stress and non-stress condition, essentially confirming the findings of the MIDIS experiment.

We are presently conducting a further stress experiment with MIDIS that replicates the earlier study with a number of important modifications. First, rather than infer stress effects upon cognitive components such as working memory and spatial ability from decision-making proficiency, such effects are measured directly and outside the criterion task as Stokes and Raby (1989) have reported. As part of this effort, changes in performance on knowledge representation tasks due to stress are also measured. Figure 4 shows the co-located IBM AT/InfoWindow and IBM PS2 installation that permit the stress manipulations and environmental conditions to be identical for both MIDIS and SPARTANS runs.

Second, the present study uses a within-subjects design and two different MIDIS flights (stressed and non-stressed in a counter-balanced design). This obviates the need to attempt to match pairs of pilots in order to run stressed and unstressed groups on a single criterion flight. Third, the stress manipulations adhere more closely to the cognitive appraisal model of stress and involve an exact replication of noise-stress conditions found to simulate anxiety in their effects upon performance (Hockey, 1986). Last, the present study contrasts novice and expert IFR pilots, as in our initial experiment, rather than observing a relatively homogeneous set of low-time pilots as in the first stress study. We anticipate that these changes will permit us to observe the extent to which stress induces (domain-independent) cognitive performance decrements in experts and novices and the extent to which these effects are reproduced (or resisted) by experts and novices in decision performance in the simulated operational setting.

Figure 4. MIDIS InfoWindow installation (left) with
SPARTANS installation (right)

ACKNOWLEDGEMENTS

This work was funded by the University of Illinois Research Board and the Armstrong Aeromedical Research Laboratory, United States Air Force. Gary Reid was the technical monitor. The author wishes to thank Dr Christopher Wickens and Dr Barbara Barnett for their academic contributions to this work, Tak Ming Lo and Robert Rosenblum for programming support, and Bert Henne, Dr Fred Hyman and Thomas Davis Jr for the development of simulated flights.

REFERENCES

Barnett, B. (1989). Information processing components and knowledge representations: An individual differences approach to modelling pilot judgement. *Proceedings of the Human Factors Society 33rd Annual Meeting,* October 1989.

Buch, G. and Diehl, A. (1984). An investigation of the effectiveness of pilot judgement training. *Human Factors,* 26, 557-564.

Doran, J.E. & Mitchie, D. (1966). Experiments with the graph traverser program. *Proceedings of the Royal Society (A),* 294, 235-259.

Einhorn, H.J. and Hogarth, R.M. (1981). Behavioural decisions theory: Process of judgement and choice. *Annual Review of Psychology,* 32, 53-88.

Friedman, L., Howell, W.C., and Jensen, C.R. (1985). Diagnostic judgement as a function of the preprocessing of evidence. *Human Factors,* 27, 665-673.

Gettys, C.F. (1983). *Research and Theory on Predecision Processes.* Technical Report TR 11-30-83, Dept. of Psychology, University of Oklahoma, Norman, OK.

Giffen, W.C. and Rockwell, T.H. (1987). A methodology for research on VFR flight into VMC. In R.S. Jensen (Ed.), *Proceedings of the Fourth Symposium on Aviation Psychology,* Columbus, Ohio.

Goldsmith, T.E. and Schvaneveldt, R.W. (1985). *ACES: Air Combat Expert Simulation.* Computing Research Laboratory Report MCCS-85-34, New Mexico State University, Las Cruces, NM.

Hockey, G.J.R. (1986). Changes in operator efficiency. In K. Boff, L. Kaufman, & J. Thomas (Eds.), *Handbook of Perception & Performance,* Vol. II. New York: John Wiley & Sons.

Hopf-Weichel, R., Lucaccini, L., Saleh, J., and Freedy, A. (1979). *Aircraft Emergency Decisions: Cognitive and Situational Variables.* Perceptronics Report PATR-1065-79-7, Perceptronics Inc., CA.

Jensen, R.S. (1982). Pilot judgement: Training and evaluation. *Human Factors,* 24, 61-73.

Kahneman, D., Slovic, P., and Tversky, A. (Eds.) (1982). *Judgement Under Uncertainty: Heuristics and Biases.* New York: Cambridge

University Press.

Maher, J.W. (1989). *Beyond CRM to decisional heuristics: An airline generated model to examine accidents and incidents caused by crew errors in deciding.* Paper presented at the 5th Symposium of the Association of Aviation Psychology, Columbus, Ohio.

Saleh, J., Thomas, J.O., and Boylan, R.J. (1979) *Identification of Significant Aircrew Decisions in Navy Aircraft.* Perceptronics Report PFTR-1075-6, Perceptronics Inc., CA.

Simmel, E.C. and Shelton, R. (1987). The assessment of nonroutine situations by pilots: A two-part process. *Aviation, Space and Environmental Medicine,* 58, 1119- 1121.

Slovic, P., Fischoff, B., and Lichtenstein, S. (1977). Behavioural decision theory. *Annual Review of Psychology,* 28, 1-39.

Slovic, P. (1982). Toward understanding and improving decisions. In W.C. Howell and E.A. Fleischman (Eds.), *Human Performance and Productivity, Vol. 2. Human Information Processing and Decision Making.* Hillsdale, NJ: Erlbaum.

Sternberg, S. (1975). Memory scanning: New findings and current controversies. *Quarterly Journal of Experimental Psychology,* 27, 1-32.

Stokes, A.F., Banich, M.T., Elledge, V., and Ke, Y. (1988). *Cognitive Function Evaluation in the Medical Certification of Airmen.* Aviation Research Laboratory Technical Report ARL-88-4/FAA-88-2, Civil Aeromedical Institute, Federal Aviation Administration, Oklahoma City, OK.

Stokes, A.F., Barnett, B., and Wickens, C.D. (1987). Modelling stress and bias in pilot decision-making. *Proceedings of the Human Factors Association of Canada, XXth Annual Conference,* Montreal, Oct 14th-17th, 45-48.

Stokes, A.F. and Raby, M. (1989). Stress and cognitive performance in trainee pilots. *Proceedings of the Human Factors Society 33rd Annual Meeting,* October 1989.

Wickens, C.D. and Flach, J. (1988). Human information processing. In E. Wiener and D. Nagel (Eds.), *Human Factors in Aviation.* New York: Wiley.

Wickens, C.D., Stokes, A.F., Barnett, B. and Davis, T. (1988). *A Componential Analysis of Pilot Decision Making.* Technical Report AAMRL-TR-88-017, Wright-Patterson AFB, Ohio.

Wickens, C.D., Stokes, A.F., Barnett, B, and Hyman, F. (1987). *The Effects of Stress on Pilot Judgement in a MIDIS Simulator.* Report on EG & G Idaho, Inc, Subcontract C87-101376, Aviation Research Laboratory, University of Illinois.

Wiener, E. and Nagel, D. (1988). *Human Factors in Aviation.* New York: Wiley.

13

Selection by flight simulation: Effects of anxiety on performance

Peter G.A.M. Jorna and R.T.B. Visser

ABSTRACT

Flight simulators are increasingly being applied as a selection tool, preferably for flight-naive subjects. The test procedure usually involves several flights to assess the trainability of an aspiring pilot. Performance is most often evaluated by an instructor and a positive grading is required to enter pilot training. Situational or state anxiety provoked by task demands or risk of failure could, however, reduce the validity of the procedure by impairing the candidate's capacity for information processing and learning. This study investigated the occurrence of anxiety, and its effects on the performance of high- and low-anxiety subjects. Instructor ratings were compared with objective measures of flight control. State anxiety was found to be increased, particularly by a differential response of subjects to removal of feedback. Anxiety did not influence deviations from the flightpath, i.e. maintaining heading and altitude, but aileron control proved to be quite different. A surprising result was that instructors significantly favoured the high state-anxious subjects. These higher ratings were not supported by objective measures of performance.

INTRODUCTION

Pilot selection typically involves two major stages for assessing pilot aptitude. The first stage involves basic personality, intelligence and psychomotor testing and is intended to assess the basic 'ability' requirements for pilots. During training, however, abilities often prove to be 'necessary but not sufficient' to develop adequate piloting skills. The reasons for such disparity can be several but are most often related to the multi-task or integrative nature of flying skills. Many countries therefore decided to use a flight simulator as a second step in the selection process. The purpose is to test the candidate's potential for acquiring skills in a limited period of time, i.e. his/her 'trainability'. A representative sample of flight tasks is presented and progress in performance is monitored. The flight grading in the Netherlands represents an important and decisive step in the selection process and experience with civilian and Navy candidates has shown that fail ratios of about fifty percent are the rule rather than the exception. This knowledge can provide the candidate with considerable uncertainty about his chances of becoming a pilot. The issue of evaluative anxiety or 'testitis' has already been recognized as relevant for performance in flight training itself (O'Connor, 1975; Smith & Melton, 1978; Krahenbuhl, 1981) but the present pilot shortages initiated a similar interest in the effects of anxiety on performance in pilot selection procedures that employ simulator training for assessing pilot aptitude. The question is whether anxiety will indeed occur, and whether it will influence the validity of the selection by producing 'false negatives'.

In this study we evaluated whether the flight grading of the government school of aviation could serve as a potential stressor by investigating the occurrence of anxiety just prior to executing simulator missions and a non-evaluative pilot aptitude test that served as a control condition (Jorna, 1989). The performance effects were evaluated by instructor ratings and objective measures of flight performance. The experiment reported here formed part of a more general research programme on the effects of mental load on pilot performance, and was performed according to a 'double blind' procedure in which neither the experimenter nor instructor had prior knowledge of the subjects' anxiety scores.

After a short introduction to the grading procedure itself, we will report the results in two sections: the first will address the trends of anxiety as observed during the flight grading, together with some probable causes, while the second section will report on the effects on subjective and objective measures of performance, by contrasting two groups of subjects, one with a relatively high level of anxiety and one with a low level as defined by the State-Trait Anxiety Inventory (STAI) designed by Spielberger (1972).

Flight simulator test procedure
The simulator is a single seat, IFR-equipped general aviation trainer (Cessna-152) mounted on a simple motion platform with three degrees of freedom. The cockpit windows are darkened and communication with the instructor is provided by a radio. The separate instructor console presents a video image of the flight instruments and a plot facility of the track flown by the aircraft. The simulator was modified for the experiment to enable continuous recording of flight parameters and pilot input control movements.

The test procedure was based on a total of six simulator flights distributed across four days. Each flight had a duration of about fifty minutes. The instructor provided instruction on the first two flights. Thereafter, commands were restricted to manoeuvres to be executed by the candidate. All tasks were rated and the instructor provided an overall grading after the third and fifth session. The lowest grading was 4 (below standard) and the highest 8 (above standard). The sixth and last session was devoted to a separate check-ride by a second instructor who did not take part in the instruction of the candidate. No feedback was provided to the candidates concerning performance level or grades assigned to them.

The flight tasks included basic manoeuvres such as take-off, straight and level flight, power settings, turning and banking etc. An additional standardized circuit pattern was added for the purpose of this study. The pattern consisted of a full rate-one turn to the left, straight and level flight with specified heading, and a full rate-one turn to the right. This manoeuvre took about six minutes to perform.

All candidates were pre-selected by the basic psychological procedures used for civil aviation in the Netherlands, and therefore represented a homogeneous sample of aspiring pilots with a restricted range in anxiety proneness. Their age range was 17-20 years and they were generally flight-naive.

Flight grading as a stressor

According to Spielberger's (1972) general theory of anxiety, there is a valid distinction between trait anxiety, which represents relatively stable individual differences in anxiety proneness, and state anxiety, which is induced by a specific environmental stressor and is accompanied by conscious feelings of tension and apprehension. The degree of state anxiety is interactively determined by the individual's susceptibility (trait) and the amount of stress in the situation. The first part of this study addressed the question of whether the flight grading acts as a sufficient external stressor to evoke a rise in state anxiety, and attempted to determine the relevant situational factors. Three factors were considered: the confrontation with new and unfamiliar procedures, the effect of repeated exposure or coping, and the threat of being evaluated by an instructor. A computerized pilot aptitude test served as a non-evaluative, but unfamiliar, control condition.

The second part of the study examined the role of individual factors such as anxiety-proneness, fear of failure, and achievement motivation in determining the severity of the situational response. Two extreme groups of subjects were selected from the available data base: a high (state) anxiety group and a low anxiety group, representing samples of subjects who respectively appraised the flight grading as being stressful and non-stressful. These anxiety groups were also used in the performance study as described in the next section. During the selection of the subjects care was taken that no obvious factor other than anxiety level could influence performance. Both groups were therefore matched to provide equal levels of pilot aptitude, intelligence, and age, and they were evaluated by the same instructors. These factors can therefore be excluded as possible causes of the differential responses of the subjects to the stressor.

METHOD

Candidates participated in two conditions: (1) the general grading procedure which was unfamiliar and evaluative, and (2) a computerized pilot aptitude test (Jorna, 1987; 1989) that was unfamiliar to the subjects, but was not being evaluated by the instructor. Two dependent measures were used: the score on the Dutch translation of the state anxiety inventory (Van der Ploeg et al, 1980) and the score on the 'tension' sub-scale of the Profile of Mood States (POMS; Wald, 1984) which should represent a similar dimension of psychological state.

The 49 subjects were all males and agreed to participate by informed consent. The questionnaires were completed just prior to take-off for each simulator session as well as prior to performing the pilot aptitude test. All scores were normalized by expressing them as a percentage of the range of the scale involved. In addition, all subjects completed the trait anxiety inventory and a questionnaire assessing individual differences in 'fear of failure' and 'achievement motivation' (a version of the PMT achievement motivation test described by Hermans, 1976). All subjects were interviewed after finishing the grading to enquire whether the responses to the questionnaires were realistic or were biased by factors such as dissimulation. This private and independent interview resulted in four subjects being deleted from the data base.

From the remaining data base of 45 subjects, 20 were selected to provide a high anxiety (HA) and a low anxiety group (LA) who respectively reported the highest and lowest mean scores on state anxiety during the grading procedure. Both groups were matched for pilot aptitude, age and intelligence, as assessed by an independent selection procedure, and they encountered the same instructors.

RESULTS

Anxiety trends
The trends observed in state-anxiety and tension during the flight grading and the non-evaluative control condition are depicted in Figure 1. The grading resulted in a higher level of anxiety for both measures as compared with the control condition ($p < 0.05$). Repeated exposure, however, decreased anxiety only from the first to the second simulator session, as indicated by both dependent measures. After this initial decline, the state score increased again from the third to the last sessions ($p < 0.01$). The tension dimension reflected a similar although somewhat suppressed trend. Such trends were not observed during repeated exposure to the control condition.

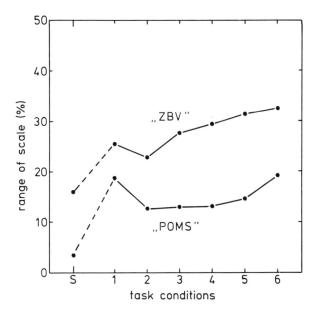

Figure 1. Trends in state anxiety score of the STAI and the 'tension'
dimension of the POMS for simulator sessions with an instructor
and a computerized pilot selection test (S) without instructor

Individual factors
The anxiety profile for the high (HA) and low anxiety (LA) groups is
depicted in Figure 2. The pattern is highly similar to the one for the entire
group, with the exception that the anxiety of the LA group did not increase
after the second simulator session. Note that both groups reported higher
levels of anxiety as compared with the pilot aptitude selection test and that
both groups reported a decline in anxiety when confronted with the
simulator for the second time.

Anxiety proneness was a relevant factor in producing these differential
responses. Scores on the trait inventory revealed a highly systematic
difference (LA group: mean = 24.6; SD = 2.6/ HA group: mean = 31.0; SD =
4.5 [p < 0.001]). Correlations obtained between trait and state scores were r
= 0.51 (ns) for the HA group and r = 0.92 (p < 0.001) for the LA group. The
scores on the factor 'Fear of Failure' were also higher for the HA group (LA:
mean = 2.5; SD = 2.0/ HA: mean = 7.1; SD = 2.0 [p < 0.02]). The HA group,
however, revealed a lower score on 'Achievement Motivation' (LA: mean =
29.1; SD = 6.9/ HA: mean = 22.9; SD = 5.3 [p < 0.02]).

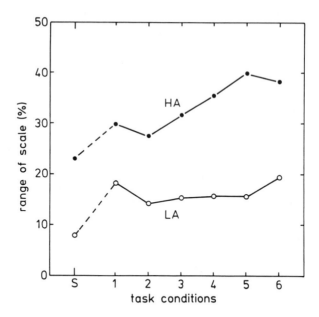

Figure 2. State-anxiety trends for experimental groups with low
and high mean levels of anxiety during the grading procedure

DISCUSSION

The results clearly indicate that the flight grading can serve as a stressor. Anxiety will typically increase during the procedure. The unfamiliarity with the task situation therefore seems to play a minor role in determining state anxiety as confirmed by the low levels of anxiety reported for the pilot selection test. Repeated exposure did not result in a general reduction of anxiety. Only the second simulator session revealed a decline in anxiety that could be attributed to familiarization. Knowledge of being evaluated contributes to the level of anxiety, as it was clearly raised at the first confrontation with the simulator and its instructor. An interesting observation was that anxiety increased gradually from the moment that the instructor stopped providing 'instruction and feedback' on how to perform the flight manoeuvres. This lack of 'knowledge of results' is apparently a dominant factor that increases state-anxiety as a function of time or sessions spent without it. A typical finding in this respect was that the LA group had a very similar anxiety pattern with one exception: the rise in anxiety after cessation of feedback. This suggests that these subjects are more self-confident and are less dependent on external feedback. This interpretation is supported by their lower scores on the 'Fear of Failure' factor and the high correlation between their state and trait anxiety scores, which indicates virtually no impact of the environmental stressor. HA subjects, however, were more anxiety-prone, had lower levels of aspiration, more fear of failure, and did react strongly to the environmental stressor, especially after cessation of the feedback. These results agree with the predictions of the interactional theory of anxiety (Spielberger, 1972; Eysenck, 1982) and provide a validation for a homogeneous pre-selected sample of subjects with relatively low anxiety scores as compared with clinical samples. Whether the differences obtained are powerful enough to affect the validity of the flight simulation can be assessed only by investigating the impact on performance level and grades received, as described in the next section.

ANXIETY AND FLIGHT PERFORMANCE

A central notion in theories of anxiety and performance is that anxiety draws upon some of the limited attentional capacity. Thus, part of the capacity is no longer available for task-relevant information processing as it has been allocated to 'worry' or other task-irrelevant information processing (Eysenck, 1982; 1983). The effects of a reduced capacity may not be apparent in performance if the subject is able to compensate for the additional demand by means of, for example, the exertion of greater effort. This will be possible only if some spare capacity remains. Anxiety effects are, however, expected to be directly related to performance in situations in which subjects are 'forced' to utilize their maximal capacity to obtain the best level of performance. The flight grading typically represents such a situation. The emotional load imposed by this evaluative 'stressor' could reduce performance or impair learning, which would conceal the true 'pilot aptitude' of the subject, as compared to normal training conditions. The aim of the present study was to assess whether such performance decrements do indeed occur with HA subjects, and whether they are relevant to the validity of the selection procedure.

Flight instructors still represent the main source of performance ratings, since the multi-dimensional nature of flying tasks creates difficulties in developing objective, simple, standardized and validated metrics of performance (Rohmann, 1983). Instructor ratings are however subjective and this will introduce variability and biases in the assessment procedure. A back-up with some objective data is therefore highly recommended (Knoop & Welde, 1973). Objective measures can be divided into two categories: 'input' measures describing the control behaviour of the pilot (aileron, rudder and elevator inputs) and 'output' measures that describe the flightpath taken by the aircraft (heading, altitude, rate of turn etc.). Deviations from actual to intended flightpath are commonly used to provide an 'accuracy' index of performance (Henry, 1974; Billings et al, 1975) but such accuracy could have been obtained by different control strategies. Separate input measures are needed because of the limited frequency response and bandwidth of the aircraft dynamics. The aircraft serves as a 'filter' that masks meaningful individual differences (Fuller et al, 1980).

In this study we used spectral analysis as a method for quantifying input control strategies of anxious and non-anxious subjects while flying a standardized circuit. According to a model proposed by Hess (1981), pilot skill will be improved by a progressive utilization of available information. This learning process should induce similar changes in control strategy as can be observed during transfer from a compensatory to a pursuit type of display which presents more information. The distinction between compensatory and pursuit behaviour is important, but sometimes confusing as it is not directly related to the physical appearance of a display, but to the information extracted from it. Compensatory behaviour can be observed with pursuit displays, if the additional error information is disregarded by the operator. Similarly, pursuit behaviour can occur with a compensatory display if the pilot can extract additional information from his knowledge of the system dynamics or the procedure of flying a standardized circuit. With either type of display, operators may adopt a relative mixture of both behaviours. Experienced pilots are, however, expected to employ more inputs in the lower-frequency part of the spectrum as they are able to act on and anticipate future events, whereas novices have to react to observed flightpath errors in a simple compensatory manner. The latter type of control should be characterized by more high-frequency, low-amplitude responses. Spectral measures in the low-frequency range were reported as most sensitive to level of skill (McDowell, 1978), possibly because compensatory or closed loop control will be required even for experienced pilots to accommodate high-precision tasks.

An interesting and appealing aspect of the outlined model is that it provides a dynamic and reversible link between information processing and tracking behaviour. A regression in control strategy is expected to occur if: (a) the information is reduced externally, e.g. as in driving a car through sudden fog, which will change the task from 'following the road' to 'keeping the car on it', and (b) the quality of information processing itself is hampered, as hypothesized to occur with anxiety under high workload conditions.

METHOD

The same extreme HA and LA groups of subjects were used as described in the first section. They performed a standardized flight task in the fifth simulator session which included a full rate-one turn to the left, straight and level flight, and a rate-one turn to the right. The simulator was instrumented to record aileron, rudder and elevator signals as well as rate of turn, rate of climb and rate of descent. All segments were analysed separately to provide absolute and root mean square (rms) deviation scores from the ideal track, and these were averaged to provide a general estimate of accuracy for this flight circuit. A similar procedure was used for the input signals for which an averaged standard deviation score was calculated. Spectral analysis was performed on the total aileron signal and power was calculated over a bandwidth of 0.5 Hz, divided over eight frequency bands. Instructors scored the performance of subjects and provided a specific and an overall grading. The subjects also evaluated their own performance. Non-parametric statistical procedures were used for data analysis.

RESULTS

Flightpath accuracy
The rms scores obtained for maintaining 'rate of turn' and 'rate of climb' are depicted in Figure 3 for both the HA and LA groups. No significant differences in flightpath accuracy were found between groups. The averaged absolute deviations from the 'ideal' track were generally small and could be regarded as excellent for flight-naive subjects. Rate of turn deviations averaged 5 degrees/minute and rate of climb deviations 50 feet/minute. No significant effect of groups was found for this measure.

Control behaviour
The averaged standard deviation (SD) scores obtained for rudder and elevator signals are depicted in Figure 4.

The group effect was significant ($p < 0.01$) for the SD score of the aileron, with higher variations in control for the LA group. A similar but marginal trend (ns) was observed for the elevator signal. Spectral analysis of the aileron signal revealed that this performance difference was consistently present across all frequency bands as depicted in Figure 5.

The difference in control behaviour was largest for the lower-frequency part of the spectrum and decreased at the higher frequencies. For all bands systematic differences were observed ($p < 0.01$).

Instructor ratings
Both the instructor and the subject provided independent ratings of performance. The averaged grades obtained during the fifth simulator session are depicted in the left panel of Figure 6. These data can be compared with similar but independent data obtained during the final grading procedure as reported after evaluating all simulator sessions.

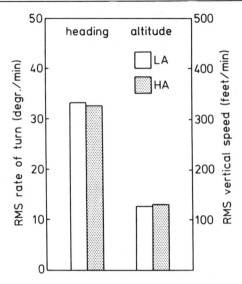

Figure 3. Deviations of flightpath for maintaining 'heading and altitude'
while flying a circuit pattern. HA = high anxiety group and LA =
low anxiety group

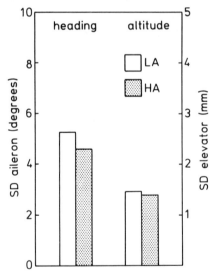

Figure 4. Global variation in input control measures for maintaining
'heading and altitude' while flying a circuit pattern. HA = high
anxiety group and LA = low anxiety group

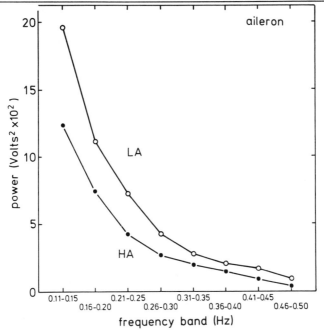

Figure 5. Power of the aileron signal in eight frequency bands for
high (HA) and low anxiety (LA) groups

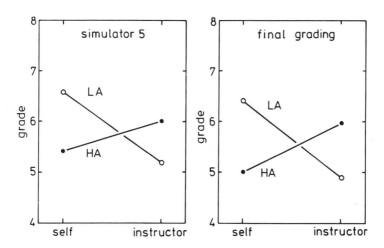

Figure 6. Self-reported estimates of performance and actual instructor
grades for high (HA) and low anxiety (LA) groups in a specific
simulator session, and an assessment of overall performance

The HA group's self-assessment of performance was lower than that of the LA group ($p < 0.01$). Instructors, however, rated the HA group as superior to the LA group ($p < 0.01$). This was a surprising result, that proved to be highly systematic as it was also observed in the grades obtained for the final grading. The preference of the instructors for the HA group was even more pronounced and the reliability of the distinction was increased as indicated by the level of significance obtained ($p < 0.005$).

DISCUSSION

State-anxiety, as manifested by the HA group, had no effect on flightpath accuracy measures, whereas pilot-input control measures revealed a clear effect of anxiety. These observations were not available to the instructor and cannot serve as a possible explanation for the positive bias found for HA subjects. This was clearly an unexpected result and it is contradictory to the general assumptions made in pilot selection. Normally, the idea is to reduce anxiety proneness in order to prevent stress reactions during the criterion task. The response of the HA subjects was, however, only marginally related to trait-anxiety, which indicates a specific and fairly independent response to this situation. A possible explanation for the bias is that instructors are sensitive to a factor such as 'eagerness' or 'perceived motivation'. It can be argued that the (extreme) low anxiety subjects exhibited relaxed behaviour that could be interpreted as insufficient motivation. This remains speculative and should be confirmed by behavioural observations during such procedures. Recent studies suggested that anxiety could serve as a motivating agent, in the sense that behaviour is adapted to reduce the uncertainty of the situation (Schulz & Schönpflug, 1988), but it is still a matter of research to assess in what way instructors or observers interpret such behaviour. The present study clearly confirmed that there are biases in these types of selection procedure and that objective measures are clearly required, not only for reasons of supporting the instructors, but also to provide unbiased criterion information for the validation of experimental selection tests.

Pilot input control was found to be more sensitive to individual differences in mental load as compared with the flightpath measures of the aircraft that include the filtering aspects of the specific dynamics of the aircraft. The predicted occurrence of 'compensatory' input behaviour for HA subjects was confirmed by the reduced power in the spectrum of the aileron signal, especially in the lower frequency range. However, a clear interpretation of such behaviour should require not only a difference in amplitude of the control response, but also a shift in frequency. Such a shift or difference between groups was not observed in the data. An alternative explanation that would fit these data is that a reduction in information processing capacity will simply reduce the opportunity, or time available, for making control actions. As a consequence of mental load, control effort simply has to be reduced, and such a model would predict an overall reduction in control activity. A regression in the quality of input control strategy, i.e. a change from pursuit to compensatory tracking mode, would also predict a specific change in frequency characteristics of the response. This issue could be resolved by a fine-grained analysis of the effect of dual task loading on the frequency and gain characteristics of 'ad libidum' input control. For the moment we have to conclude that pilot input control measures offer promise for studies of mental load, but that further research is needed to improve the interpretation of specific changes in control behaviour or strategy.

REFERENCES

Billings, C.E., Gerke, R.J., and Wick, R.L. (1975). Comparisons of pilot performance in simulated and actual flight. *Aviation, Space and Environmental Medicine*, 46, 304-308.

Eysenck, M.W. (1982). *Attention and Arousal: Cognition and Performance*. Berlin: Springer Verlag.

Eysenck, M.W. (1983). Anxiety and individual differences. In R. Hockey (Ed.), *Stress and Fatigue in Human Performance*. New York: John Wiley.

Fuller, J.H., Waag, W.L., and Martin, E.L. (1980). *Advanced Simulator for Pilot Training: Design of Automated Performance Measurement System*. Wright-Patterson AFB, Ohio: Air Force Human Resources Laboratory, Report No. AFHRL-TR-79-57.

Henry, P.H. (1974). *An Automated System to Assess Pilot Performance in a Link GAT-1 trainer*. Brooks AFB, Texas: School of Aerospace Medicine Report.

Hermans, H.J.M. (1976). *PMT-Prestatie Motivatie Test: Handleiding*. Amsterdam: Swets & Zeitlinger.

Hess, R.A. (1981). Pursuit tracking and higher levels of skill development in the human pilot. *IEEE Transactions on Systems, Man and Cybernetics*, 4, 262-273.

Jorna, P.G.A.M. (1987). *Selection of pilots based on dual-task performance*. In Proceedings of the 17th Conference of the Western European Association for Aviation Psychology. Baden, Austria: WEAAP.

Jorna, P.G.A.M. (1989). Prediction of success in flight training by single- and dual-task performance. In *Human Behaviour in High Stress Situations in Aerospace Operations*. Neuilly-sur-Seine: AGARD Report No. CP-458.

Knoop, P.A. and Welde, W.L. (1973). *Automated Pilot Performance Assessment in the T-37: A Feasibility Study*. Wright-Patterson AFB, Ohio: Air Force Human Resources Laboratory, Report No. AFHRL-TR-72-6.

Krahenbuhl, G.S. (1981). Instructor pilot teaching behavior and student pilot stress in flight training. *Aviation, Space and Environmental Medicine,* 52, 594-597.

McDowell, E.D. (1978). *The Development and Evaluation of Objective Frequency Domain Based Pilot Performance Measures in ASUPT.* Oregon: Oregon State University, Report No. AFOSR-TR-78-1239.

O'Connor, P.J. (1975). Testitis: excessive anxiety about flying checks. *Aviation, Space and Environmental Medicine,* 46, 1407-1409.

Ploeg, H.M., van der, Defares, P.B., and Spielberger, C.D. (1980). *Handleiding bij de zelf-beoordelingsvrage nlijst.* Lisse: Swets & Zeitlinger.

Rohmann, J.T. (1983). *Pilot Performance Measurement: An Annotated Bibliography.* Washington, DC: U.S. Department of Transportation (FAA), Report No DOT/FAA/CT-82/24.

Schulz, P. and Schönpflug, W. (1988). Anxiety as a motivating factor and stressing agent. In C.D. Spielberger and P.B. Defares (Eds.), *Stress and Anxiety, Vol 11.* Washington, DC: Hemisphere Publishing.

Smith, R.C. and Melton, C.E. (1978). Effects of ground trainer use on the anxiety of students in private pilot training. *Aviation, Space and Environmental Medicine,* 48, 856-858.

Spielberger, C.D. (1972). Anxiety as an emotional state. In: C.D. Spielberger (Ed.), *Anxiety: Current Trends in Theory and Research, Vol 1.* New York: Academic Press.

Wald, F.D.M. (1984). An Abbreviated Version of the Profile of Mood States (POMS) questionnaire. Doctoral Thesis, Department of Psychophysiology, University of Amsterdam.

Part III

Operational Issues

14

Giving the pilot two sources of information: Help or hindrance?

Stephen J. Selcon, Robert M. Taylor, and Roy A. Shadrake

SUMMARY

This paper addresses the nature and levels of processing involved when information from one source is integrated with a supposedly redundant secondary source to provide a performance gain in choice reaction time (RT) tasks. Consideration is given to the benefits for comprehension arising from this 'redundancy gain' effect, which are assessed within both a theoretical framework and the applied context of aircrew systems design. Three experiments are described that were intended to investigate redundancy gain. The first explored the use of feedback to a Direct Voice Input (DVI) system, using bi-modal (visual/verbal) presentation of simple printed digits/spoken numbers to establish the presence of cross-modal integrality. The second used colours, words, and combinations of both with shared semantic associations to determine whether or not redundancy gain occurs at the level of 'comprehension'. The third used warning 'icons' (pictorial representations of danger situations) and verbal warning messages. The icons were generated by aircrew as meaningful visual representations of cockpit warnings. The high level of abstraction of these icons would strongly imply that any performance gain occurring must result from the integration of 'information' rather than 'data'. Measures of both 'speed' and 'depth' of comprehension were taken. The results of these experiments are considered in terms of current information processing and neural network theories, and a cognitive model of this integrality effect is described. The use of this integrality paradigm as a systems design methodology is discussed.

INTRODUCTION

Morton (1969) demonstrated that the provision of simultaneous, correlated, visual stimulus information produced a performance gain in a card sorting task. This he attributed to a combination of the information from the two sources allowing reduced parallel processing of each, and hence reduced processing time. Similarly, Garner and Felfoldy (1970) reported that under

139

some circumstances facilitation occurred with multi-dimensional visual stimuli when the information on the different dimensions was correlated, and interference when it was uncorrelated. They suggested that these effects depended upon the dimensions being 'integral'; when they were 'separable', neither facilitation nor interference was observed.

We have applied the concept of redundancy gain to the design of visual displays (Taylor, 1984). The locus of this effect, however, was considered to be within the perceptual domain, with little consideration given to the possibility of a cognitive analogue of the integrality-separability paradigm. Kramer et al (1985), however, investigated dual-task integrality by taking EEG measures of activity. They found that, when events in the two tasks were correlated, there was a facilitation effect, thus implying that the two tasks were integral. A cross-modal integrality effect was demonstrated by MacDonald and McGurk (1978). They presented contradictory phonemic and articulatory information simultaneously to subjects and found that inappropriate articulation (uncorrelated speaker lip movements) changed the phoneme that was perceived. This implies that information was integrated across the two modalities during perceptual decoding, thus affecting the resultant perception. The locus of the effect is still at the perceptual level of processing, however, with no apparent relevance to deeper, more 'cognitive', processes.

The three experiments described in this chapter set out to ascertain whether cognitive integrality exists and, if so, the level of processing at which it occurs. By looking for facilitation from a redundant secondary information source, it was hoped to show that information can be used integrally both within and across modalities in the decision process, i.e. that it can be integrated from uni/multi-modal simultaneous presentation, thus enabling a decision on its 'meaning' to be made more quickly. The implication of such an effect would be that the presentation of simultaneous visual and verbal information by cockpit systems would help the user to understand, and respond to, the feedback message more quickly. This in turn would imply a reduction in processing time, thus leading to a possible reduction in workload. It was also hoped to show that an increase in depth of understanding can accrue from such integral information. This has particularly important implications for the design of highly critical aircrew systems, such as warning systems.

EXPERIMENT ONE: DIRECT VOICE INPUT (DVI) SYSTEM FEEDBACK

Introduction
This study was undertaken to examine the requirement for, and any performance benefits arising from, the use of correlated visual and auditory feedback to a Direct Voice Input (DVI) system. Human engineering issues are particularly relevant to the applicability of DVI technology to the

military single-seat cockpit (see Berman, 1984, for an overview). One such consideration must be the requirement for, and nature of, feedback to inform the user of the DVI system that his verbal input has been both received and recognized correctly. It is necessary that this feedback be presented in a mode that provides optimal understanding of message content with minimum time and workload demands on the user.

Both visual and auditory feedback alone have been criticized. The former requires visual attention, thus reducing the advantages of providing a DVI system to free visual resources; the latter is necessarily 'real-time', thus introducing delays when there is a need for successive data entries. It has been suggested that the provision of both types of feedback is preferable, since it will allow the user to gain information selectively from the source more convenient within the current operational context (McGuiness, 1987). This study attempts to show that there may be further performance benefits from the use of dual-modality feedback, arising from an integration of information during mental processing.

Method
A single digit was presented to subjects on a colour monitor. They were required to respond by reading the digit aloud into a microphone; this acted as an input to a speech recognizer, which in turn provided feedback (verbal, visual, or both simultaneously) to the subject.

Visual feedback was in the form of a white digit against a black background. Verbal feedback was digitized female speech. The bi-modal feedback was either correlated, with both types of feedback correct; uncorrelated, with one type correct; correlated, with both incorrect (the same feedback on each modality, but different from the initial stimulus); or uncorrelated, with neither correct (different feedback on each modality, neither matching the initial stimulus).

The type of feedback given was pre-programmed and hence was independent of the verbal input made by the subject to the initial stimulus. After feedback was presented, subjects were required to indicate whether at least one type of feedback had been correct. Visual feedback was presented at a time corresponding to the approximate perceptual centre of the verbal feedback; RT was measured from the presentation of the visual feedback, to ensure that any differences in RT between visual and verbal feedback conditions were not artefacts of the point from which timings were started. Eighteen non-aircrew subjects were tested, all with normal hearing and vision.

Results
Bi-modal correct correlated feedback provided significantly faster ($p < 0.05$) RTs than either visual or auditory correct feedback alone (Figure 1a). Analysis of variance (ANOVA) showed a significant ($p < 0.001$) main effect

of feedback category; this factor interacted significantly (p < 0.01) with correct vs. incorrect feedback trials. On correct feedback trials, RTs with bi-modal correlated feedback were significantly faster (p < 0.01) than those with visual feedback only, which were in turn significantly faster than those in the other three conditions (p < 0.01). The advantage for bi-modal correlated feedback indicates a redundancy gain.

A cross-modality interference effect can be seen with bi-modal uncorrelated feedback (i.e. with only one correct source of feedback). RTs with bi-modal uncorrelated feedback were significantly slower than those with bi-modal correlated and uni-modal visual feedback (p < 0.01). The slowest RTs were found in the bi-modal correlated incorrect condition (Figure 1b), suggesting that information from the supposedly redundant secondary source was integrated with information from the first to provide a 'negative redundancy gain' effect, i.e. strongly to prime an inappropriate 'yes' response that was then difficult to reject.

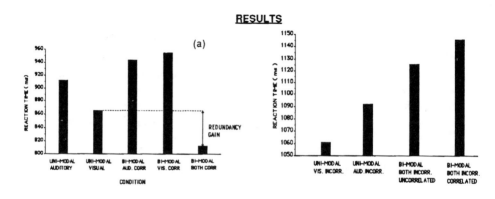

Figure 1. Mean RTs on (a) correct and (b) incorrect DVI feedback trials

Discussion

The above results clearly show that, when correlated feedback is presented to two modalities simultaneously, a redundancy gain occurs. This strongly suggests that the information contained in the two sources of feedback is integral; further, it is evidence that the effect occurs at a cognitive, rather than a perceptual, level, since no integration is possible at a perceptual level when the information is presented across two modalities. From this experiment alone, it is difficult to provide a complete model of the processes of cognitive integrality.

Two general explanations of the effect seem possible. Firstly, it can be modelled in terms of the integration of information at the level of lexical access. Information from the matched inputs can be processed in parallel, and fed simultaneously into a logogen-type system, thus producing a reduction in the amount of processing time needed, since the logogen acceptance criterion will be reached more quickly with two simultaneous inputs of information. The locus of this effect can be considered an essentially pre-comprehensive level of processing.

A second explanation might be that the inputs are combined at a post-comprehensive stage of processing. This model would suggest that independent, parallel comprehension of the stimuli occurs, but that information from the two sources is fed into the decision-making process, thus reaching a decision criterion more quickly and, therefore, reducing RT. Since the correlated feedback used in this study was directly matched (e.g. the visual digit 4 and the auditory signal 'four'), no clear indication of which theory is correct emerges.

Some resolution of this ambiguity can be achieved from the results of the trials using incorrect feedback. The increased RT in the correlated incorrect feedback condition would suggest that integration occurs at the post-comprehensive level: a unitary logogen feeding into the decision process should require less processing to reject than two different but incorrect logogens, whereas the results indicate the opposite trend. Moreover, the output of two identical logogens should take longer to reject since they produce a larger data mismatch that must be rejected to reach the appropriate decision. This is reflected in the longer RTs to the incorrect correlated condition. It is important to note that, since not all the differences between the incorrect feedback conditions reached significance at the 5% level, this interpretation can be only tentative.

EXPERIMENT TWO: COLOUR WARNING LEGENDS

Introduction

The use of red coloration for priority cockpit warning legends has long been accepted (see Boff and Lincoln, 1987, for an overview). However, it has proved difficult to engineer a red compatible with night vision goggles (NVGs).

There is little experimental evidence for the necessity of using red with warning messages, the design recommendation for its use being intuitive rather than empirically based. This experiment investigated whether there was a performance benefit in presenting cockpit warning legends in red, and probed further the levels of processing at which any integrality, if present, might exist. A categorization task was used in which the word meanings were correlated/uncorrelated with the intuitive meaning of their colour. Thus any integrality effect observed must occur after access to semantic information about both the words and colours, implying a redundancy gain at the level of comprehension or beyond.

Method

Subjects were presented on a computer monitor with words having semantic associations with 'danger' (e.g. threat, hazard) or 'safety' (e.g. safe, calm), or 'neutral' words (e.g. table, chair). Words in each category were matched for word length and frequency; they were presented in red, green, or white, against a black background. Red was chosen as being intuitively linked with danger, and green with safety. White was chosen as having no obvious intuitive associations with any of the word categories.

Each word category was presented in each colour. Subjects were required to categorize the words shown as either danger, safety, or neutral words by means of a three-key response box, regardless of the ink colour in which they were presented. RTs were measured. Eighteen non-aircrew were tested, all with normal or corrected vision.

Results

As Table 1 shows, danger words were categorized significantly more rapidly ($p < 0.01$) when they were presented in red than in either of the other colours, and danger words in green were categorized most slowly ($p < 0.05$). Conversely, safety words were categorized more rapidly when presented in green than in red ($p < 0.05$). This implies that information from the redundant colour coding is processed integrally with the linguistic information, providing a redundancy gain for the correlated conditions.

Neutral words were categorized more quickly in white than in the other colours ($p < 0.05$). Since associations between the neutral words and the neutral colour are unlikely to be present, this would imply that interference is being introduced into the processing of the neutral words by the presence of an uncorrelated colour coding.

Table 1. Mean RTs for word category/colour conditions

	Red	Green	White
Danger	0.909	1.130	1.016
Safe	1.343	1.268	1.468
Neutral	1.180	1.038	0.986

Discussion

The redundancy gain effect apparent in these results implies that integral processing of the linguistic and colour coding information occurred. Since the link between the two sources of information is only at the semantic association level, the integration of the information must occur at or beyond this level of processing. This supports the finding in Experiment One that cognitive integrality can exist at advanced stages of processing with potential benefits for the speed of understanding of information available to system operators. It does not, however, give any indication of potential benefits to 'depth' of understanding that might be expected from integration of redundant material during decision making. Experiment Three addresses this issue.

EXPERIMENT THREE: VISUAL AND VERBAL WARNING ICONS

Introduction

Helmet Mounted Display (HMD) technology offers a facility for presentation of graphical warnings to the pilot at his locus of fixation. These could take the form of visual 'icons' or pictures of the relevant warning situation. The availability of voice technology in the cockpit also allows the generation of speech icons or verbal warning messages for presentation. The aim of both types of warning is to inform the pilot as quickly as possible of the nature of the problem, allowing him to take correct remedial action immediately. Thus both speed and depth of understanding are important for the pilot to understand and act quickly and correctly. Experiment Three investigated the use of integral bi-modal information presentation as a method of improving this understanding; it was hoped to demonstrate integrality even with highly abstract information representations across two modalities.

Method

Subjects were presented with either visual, auditory, or both types of warning icon describing real aircraft 'warning' (high priority/threat) and 'caution' (low priority/threat) situations. The visual icons were generated by aircrew as meaningful representations of those situations. The verbal warning messages were based on the F/A18 voice warning system and described the same warnings/cautions as the visual icons. Where both types of icon were presented simultaneously, the situations given in each modality were always matched. Subjects were asked to classify each situation as either 'warning' or 'caution' and then to rate the threat associated with it. RTs were taken from the onset of the verbal messages. Subjects were also required to complete a three-dimensional SART (Situation Awareness Rating Technique; Taylor, 1988) rating for each stimulus.

Twelve non-aircrew subjects were tested, all with normal hearing and vision. Training was given to subjects prior to the experiment to ensure that the situations presented would be meaningful to them.

Results

Table 2 shows that the shortest RTs were produced by the visual icons (p < 0.01), with RTs in the 'both' condition being faster than with the verbal icons alone (p < 0.05). This was contrary to the prediction of integrality that the shortest RT would occur in the 'both' condition, and is perhaps attributable to a baseline increase in RT introduced by the length of the voice messages because of the arbitrary point from which timings were taken. This was confirmed during de-brief of subjects, some of whom reported waiting until the message was completed before responding even when understanding had been achieved, and is further supported by the results obtained from the 3D SART scores. It can be seen from these that Understanding was rated as significantly higher for the 'both' condition, supporting the integrality hypothesis ($p < 0.05$). The Understanding rating also correlated significantly with RT within conditions ($r = -0.38$, $p < 0.05$), implying that increased understanding reduces RT and that between-condition differences in RT are likely to be the result of experimental artefacts.

Table 2. Mean RTs and SART scores in Experiment Three

	Visual	Auditory	Both
RT (sec)	1.64	2.08	1.83
SART ratings			
Demand	43.82	50.81	45.97
Supply	55.28	57.37	53.34
Understanding	71.79	73.90	74.76

Discussion

The results of Experiment Three provide further support for the existence of cognitive integrality; however, they must be interpreted cautiously because of the probable presence of an artefact in the RT measure. It is apparent, however, that subjective understanding is improved by the presence of the two sources of information, with consequent implications for the situational awareness of the pilot. Further research is required (using shorter voice messages) to develop a complete picture, but it seems likely that for high priority warning situations a benefit in understanding and hence operator performance can be achieved by the use of integral bi-modal information design. It also seems clear that this redundancy gain is available even with abstract information and at relatively deep levels of processing.

GENERAL DISCUSSION

The results of these experiments indicate that information, both within and between modalities, can be processed integrally to produce performance benefits. This integrality appears to exist at relatively deep levels of processing and can therefore be thought of as genuinely cognitive in origin. As mentioned previously, however, the integrality effect is also apparent during perceptual and primary encoding stages of processing.

'Perceptual' and 'cognitive' integrality may represent a unitary mechanism, the level at which integration occurs being determined by the earliest stage of processing at which integrality is useful. This notion can be modelled in terms of McClelland and Rumelhardt's (1986) theory of parallel distributed processing. If it is assumed that there is a single neural network subserving a common set of knowledge structures, with information from various channels being directed towards this 'central executive', then parsimony would dictate that the point at which integrality occurs will be dependent on the level of the network at which a common neural pathway becomes available.

If the two sources of information use a common pathway from early in the processing (e.g. the colour and brightness dimensions of a visual stimulus), then the redundancy gain effect will manifest itself at an apparently 'perceptual' level. If, however, the information travels down separate pathways until late in the processing (e.g. word and colour meaning) then the redundancy gain will be seen during the post-comprehensive or decision-making stage. This is an important consideration in aircrew systems design since apparently separate information, drawing on separate attentional resource pools (Wickens, 1984), may indeed be integral at advanced stages of processing. Potential advantages to the system user can be identified, both in understanding and situational awareness, and can be exploited by the designer.

The combination of an attentional model approach with an underlying processing model (including an integrality component) should mean that greater accuracy and flexibility will be available to the human factors engineer in a priori considerations of information requirements and input/output modality demands.

REFERENCES

Berman, J.V.F. (1984). *Speech Recognition Systems in High Performance Aircraft: Some Human Factors Considerations.* RAF IAM Report No. 646. Farnborough, UK: RAF Institute of Aviation Medicine.

Boff, K.R. and Lincoln, J.E. (1988). *Engineering Data Compendium: Human Perception and Performance.* New York: Wiley.

Garner, W.R. and Felfoldy, G.L. (1970). Integrality of stimulus dimensions in various types of information processing. *Cognitive Psychology,* 1, 225-241.

Kramer, A.F., Wickens, C.D., and Donchin, E. (1985). Processing of stimulus properties: Evidence for dual task integrality. *Journal of Experimental Psychology,* 1, 393-408.

MacDonald, J. and McGurk, H. (1978). Visual influences on speech perception processes. *Perception and Psychophysics,* 24, 253-257.

McClelland, J.L. and Rumelhardt, D.E. (1986). *Parallel Distributed Processing: Explorations in the Microstructure of Cognition, Vol. 1: Psychological and Biological Models.* Cambridge: Cambridge University Press.

McGuiness, B. (1987). *Effects of Speech Recognition Modality in an Airborne Voice Communications Task.* Royal Aircraft Establishment Technical Report No. 87072. Farnborough, UK: Royal Aircraft Establishment.

Morton, J. (1969). The use of correlated stimulus information in card sorting. *Perception and Psychophysics,* 5, 374-376.

Taylor, R.M. (1984). Some effects of display format variables on the perception of aircraft spatial orientation. In AGARD-CP-371: *Human Factors Considerations in High Performance Aircraft.* Neuilly-sur-Seine: NATO Advisory Group on Aerospace Research and Development.

Taylor, R.M. (1988). Trust and awareness in human-electronic crew teamwork. In *Proceedings of the Workshop on the Human-Electronic Crew,* Ingolstadt, FRG.

Wickens, C.D. (1984). *Engineering Psychology and Human Performance.* Columbus: Merrill.

15

Attitudes towards a no smoking trial on MoD chartered flights

Susan E. Dale, James L. Wilbourn, and Paddy G. C. Tapsfield

ABSTRACT

An increase in complaints about smoking on MoD (RAF) charter flights led to the Joint Committee Air Transport Services (JCATS) instigating a trial smoking ban on flights between the UK and Germany or Gibraltar. The trial ran initially for six months, beginning May 1988, but was later extended to 31 March 1989.

To gauge passenger opinion, a questionnaire was administered to all 1648 passengers on the trial services during July 1988.

The questionnaire was designed to investigate three topics: (1) attitudes towards the ban; (2) opinions as to the effectiveness of various strategies that could be employed in an attempt to reduce non-smoker discomfort; and (3) smoking habits of passengers.

This paper reports the major findings of the survey and considers implications for passenger comfort and safety. Briefly, 67.7% (1116) agreed with the smoking ban, including a large minority (35.7%) of smokers.

INTRODUCTION

Western attitudes towards smoking have changed markedly over the last 10-15 years (Shepard, 1983). This shift in public opinion has been reflected in the incidence of smoking restrictions in every type of public place. In the aviation industry these changes include the British Airways' smoking ban on all domestic flights and Air Canada's no smoking policy on all North American flights. However, there appears to be little published information about air passengers' attitudes towards in-flight smoking or a smoking ban. This is not to say that the work has not been done – simply that there may be commercial resistance to making such information widely known. This paper aims to report air passengers' opinions about a trial smoking ban. The trial was conducted on Ministry of Defence (MoD)/Royal Air Force (RAF) chartered air services.

The RAF carries about 700,000 passengers per annum on scheduled and

149

chartered services to North and South America, the South Atlantic and the Far East, as well as European destinations. Growing awareness of an ever-increasing and unacceptable level of passenger complaints about smoking on its services led the RAF to initiate a trial ban. A passenger opinion survey was sponsored to determine the feasibility of a permanent no smoking policy.

METHOD

Background
The trial ban ran initially for six months beginning May 1988. It was later extended due to its popularity.

Safety and logistic considerations restricted the trial to two chartered services that represent about half of the RAF/MoD operations. These are run by Britannia Airways on behalf of the MoD. The services are a short flight between the UK and Germany (1 hour in duration) and a longer 3.5 hour flight between the UK and Gibraltar.

The questionnaire
The survey questionnaire examines:
1. Attitudes towards the ban;
2. Opinions about the effectiveness of various strategies that could be employed in an attempt to reduce non-smoker discomfort;
3. (Where appropriate) passengers' smoking habits.

Administration
The questionnaire was administered to all 1648 passengers travelling on the trial services in July 1988. It was given to passengers during the flight by cabin staff. Completed questionnaires were returned to the staff by passengers leaving the aircraft. Administration was monitored by a psychologist.

RESULTS

The results will be presented in four sections: sample description; attitudes towards the ban; opinions on segregation strategies; and smokers' habits. The results describe the effects of smoking status and length of flight. Initially, however, the sample population will be described using available information.

The sample
The sample of 1648 passengers comprised predominantly military personnel (1306/80.5%), the remaining 19.5% consisting of 147 (9.1%) MoD civilians and 168 (10.4%) military dependants. Ninety-seven percent (1599) of the

passengers were not on their first air flight, i.e. were experienced air passengers.

Table 1 shows smoking status by length of flight. Six hundred and one passengers (36.6%) were cigarette smokers, 972 (59.3%) non-smokers, and 67 (4%) pipe or cigar smokers. There were similar proportions of smokers and non-smokers on the long (3.5 hour) and short (1 hour) flights.

Table 1. Passengers' smoking status by length of flight

Length of Flight

	Long	Short	Total
Cigarette	96 (35.7)	505 (36.8)	601 (36.6)
Pipe	5 (1.8)	22 (1.6)	27 (1.6)
Cigar	6 (1.9)	34 (2.4)	40 (2.4)
Non-smoker	162 (60.2)	810 (59.1)	972 (59.3)
Total	269 (16.4)	1371 (83.6)	1640 (100)

Percentages are shown in brackets

However, there were about five times as many passengers on the short flights as on the long flights (1371 and 269, respectively).

Attitudes to the ban

Table 2 shows that, overall, 67.7% (1100) of the sample agreed with the ban, only 23.2% (376) disagreed, and 9.1% (148) had no opinion.

As expected, more non-smokers than smokers agreed with the ban (888 [86.2%] and 212 [35.7%], respectively). More surprisingly, only 318 smokers [53.5%] disagreed with the ban.

Table 2. Attitudes towards the ban by smoking status

	Smoking Status		
	Smokers	Non-smokers	Total
Agree	212 (35.7)	888 (86.2)	1100 (67.7)
No opinion	64 (10.8)	84 (8.2)	148 (9.1)
Disagree	318 (53.5)	58 (5.6)	376 (23.2)
Total	594 (36.6)	1030 (63.3)	1624 (100)

Percentages are shown in brackets

When asked if the ban had made the flight better for all, 1144 passengers (78.1%) said 'Yes'. Even a majority of smokers (263/50.4%) agreed. Only 71 (7.2%) of non-smokers disagreed (Table 3).

Table 4 shows that for those who agree with the ban there appear to be no effects of length of flight (179 [67.0%] and 921 [67.8%] for the long and short flights, respectively). However, there does appear to be a small polarization effect, with a larger proportion of the short flight passengers (10.2%) than longer flight passengers (3.7%) registering a 'no opinion'. This is reflected in the slightly higher proportion of long flight passengers disagreeing with the ban (29.2% compared to 22.0% on the short flight).

To summarize this section, most passengers (67.7%) agreed with the ban. This includes a substantial minority (35.7%) of smokers. Length of flight appeared to have little effect on passengers' attitudes toward the ban.

Table 3. 'The ban makes the flight better for all' by smoking status

| | Smoking Status | | |
	Smokers	Non-smokers	Total
Yes	263 (50.4)	911 (92.8)	1174 (78.1)
No	259 (49.6)	71 (7.2)	330 (29.1)
Total	522 (34.7)	982 (65.3)	1504 (100)

Percentages are shown in brackets

Table 4. Attitude toward the ban by length of flight

| | Length of Flight | | |
	Long	Short	Total
Agree	179 (67.0)	921 (67.8)	1100 (67.7)
No opinion	10 (3.7)	138 (10.2)	148 (9.1)
Disagree	78 (29.2)	298 (22.0)	376 (23.2)
Total 267	(16.4)	1357 (83.6)	1624 (100)

Percentages are shown in brackets

Opinions about segregation strategies

Passengers were asked to consider the effectiveness of three strategies that could be used to alleviate non-smoker discomfort. These were physical separation, a separation screen (such as those used between first and tourist classes), and improved ventilation. The results for these questions are summarized in Tables 5 and 6; since the patterns of results for the three strategies are similar, only the responses for improved ventilation are shown.

Improved ventilation was the most highly rated strategy: 1008 passengers (63.3%) considered it satisfactory. Even a majority of non-smokers (524/51.9%) agreed. Length of flight appears to have some effect (Table 6). A slightly higher proportion of passengers on short flights considered improved ventilation a satisfactory strategy for reducing non-smoker discomfort (64.3% compared to 58.2% on the long flight).

Table 5. 'Improved ventilation' is a satisfactory
strategy by smoking status

| | Smoking Status | | |
	Smokers	Non-smokers	Total
Yes	484 (83.0)	524 (51.9)	1008 (63.3)
No	99 (17.0)	486 (48.1)	585 (36.7)
Total	583 (36.6)	1010 (63.4)	1593 (100)

Percentages are shown in brackets

Table 6. 'Improved ventilation' is a satisfactory
strategy by length of flight.

| | Length of Flight | | |
	Long	Short	Total
Yes	153 (58.2)	854 (64.3)	1007 (63.3)
No	110 (41.8)	475 (35.7)	585 (36.7)
Total	263 (16.5)	1329 (83.5)	1592 (100)

Percentages are shown in brackets

To summarize, a smaller proportion (but still a majority) of non-smokers than smokers considered the strategy of improved ventilation satisfactory (51.9% compared to 48.1% respectively). This strategy was considered satisfactory by a slightly smaller proportion of passengers on the longer flights (58.2%) than on the short flights (64.3%).

Smokers' habits

Table 7 shows the number of smokers in three daily consumption groups, together with their mean anticipated period of voluntary non-smoking.

The majority of smokers (58.2%) consume between 11 and 20 cigarettes per day. Of the remainder, 19.4% consume fewer cigarettes per day, and 22.4% consume more than 20 per day. This appears to be reflected in their anticipated maximum period of voluntary non-smoking. The mean non-smoking period for the light (0-10 per day) smokers is 4.5 hours; for the moderate group (11-20 per day) it is 3.6 hours and for the heavy smokers (21 and over per day) it is only 2.3 hours. Thus, the greater the daily consumption, the smaller is the tolerable non-smoking period.

Table 7. Numbers of passengers by daily cigarette consumption and
mean period of voluntary non-smoking (hours)

	Daily Consumption of Cigarettes			
	0-10	11-20	21 & over	Total
Number of	115	346	133	594
passengers	(19.4)	(58.2)	(22.4)	(100)
Mean non-smoking period (hours)	4.25	3.6	2.3	3.4

Percentages are shown in brackets

DISCUSSION

The results show that 67.7% of all 1648 passengers agreed with the smoking ban on the trial services. This figure appears to be fairly stable regardless of length of flight. Large differences between smoker and non-smoker opinions may be expected; however, substantial proportions of smokers registered favourable opinions about the ban (37.7% agreeing with it).

On the basis of these results the MoD has permanently banned smoking on all flights of under 3.5 hours' duration. This effectively includes flights to north west Europe, Italy, and Gibraltar. Flight safety considerations dictate that the ban must be deferred until aircraft are fitted with smoke detectors.

The analysis of passengers' smoking habits shows that most smoking passengers cannot tolerably anticipate a 3.5 hour flight (mean period was 3.4 hours). This is supported by anecdotal evidence from the organization involved in the study, whose staff have noted an increased incidence of passengers 'lighting-up' immediately after leaving the aircraft, a practice that is extremely hazardous in view of the amount of aviation fuel in the area. Consequently, passengers must be carefully supervised until they have entered airport reception buildings, implying a certain amount of increased personnel costs.

The segregation strategy most favoured by passengers was improved ventilation. Even a majority of non-smokers considered it satisfactory (51.9%). It should be noted, however, that this strategy appears to be less popular than the ban (63.3% compared to 67.7%, respectively).

As this study took its sample population from 1 hour and 3.5 hour flights only, it does not represent passengers' views on very long flights such as the transatlantic service to Washington (7 hours). The purpose of the present paper is to encourage discussion and information exchange on an issue central to passenger safety and comfort.

REFERENCE

Shepard, R.J. (1983). *The Risk of Passive Smoking.* 120 -133. Chichester: Wiley.

16

An integrated private and instrument pilot flight training programme in a university

Henry L. Taylor, Robert H. Kaiser, Sybil Phillips,
Ricky A. Weinberg and Omer Benn

ABSTRACT

The sequence of instruction approved by the Federal Aviation Administration (FAA) involves teaching beginning pilots to fly using visual reference to the ground (contact); instrument flight instruction follows the completion of contact instruction. A number of studies have investigated instrument first instruction and/or concurrent contact and instrument instruction (Lee, 1935; Ritchie & Michael, 1955; Williams, Houston, & Wilkerson, 1956; Easter & Hubbard, 1968). The latter two studies found that the integrated approach produced superior private pilots with substantial instrument flight ability but failed to produce instrument pilots.

During the past few years, the Institute of Aviation has conducted an integrated private pilot/instrument flight programme. Kaiser, Weinberg, Davis, Benn and Taylor (1986) and Taylor, Kaiser, Weinberg and Benn (1987) reported experimental programmes demonstrating that combined private/instrument pilot flight training programmes with a substantial concentration on instrument procedures at the beginning of training are effective in producing instrument pilots.

A follow-on experimental programme conducted over the last two years with thirty-nine beginning flight students compared an integrated contact/instrument experimental group (E1), an accelerated instrument flight training group (E2) and, on selected manoeuvres, a control group (C) which was enrolled in the Institute's standard private pilot (2 semesters) and commercial/instrument (4 semesters) flight training programme. All subjects completed the private pilot programme during the first year (2 semesters). Group E1 (10 subjects) was enrolled in an integrated contact/instrument training programme with substantial instrument instruction (41 hours); Groups E2 and C were enrolled in the Institute's standard private pilot curriculum with minimum instrument instruction (8 hours). For the two semesters following the completion of the private pilot rating, E1 received an additional 47 hours, E2 received 57 hours and C received 35 hours of instrument training.

Thirty-two subjects completed the four semester sequence. The subjects in the two experimental groups were given the standard FAA Instrument Rating Practical Test and the control group received the Institute's standard fourth semester stage check.

Nine of the eleven students in the control group successfully completed the stage check on the first attempt and were recommended to take the next course in the four course commercial-instrument sequence. The two students who failed the initial stage check passed the recheck. For E1, six of eight students successfully completed the check ride for the Instrument rating. The two students who failed passed the recheck. Two of thirteen of the students in E2 were not recommended for the Instrument rating but were given the check ride. In addition to these two, four additional students (six total) failed the Instrument rating check ride, while seven passed, on the first attempt. Three of the four who were recommended but failed passed the recheck while the fourth student required two rechecks before successfully completing the check ride. The 2 X 3 Chi-square to test, among the three groups, the significance of the difference in the number of students who initially passed the check ride was not significant.

Mean rating scores for all tasks in each of the six areas of the Instrument Rating Practical Test Standards were computed for each area for groups E1 and E2. Inspection indicated only minor differences between the means of the two experimental groups for any of the areas. A general linear models procedure was used to compute a MANOVA to test the significance of the difference between the two groups for the six areas. An exact F-Test based on Wilk's criterion indicated no significant difference between the two groups. The general linear models procedure was also used to compute ANOVAs for each of the six areas to test the significance of the difference between the two groups (E1 and E2) on each of the areas. None of the F-Tests indicated a significant difference between the two groups.

A Z statistic was computed to determine whether the number of subjects in E1 and E2 initially passing the Instrument rating check ride were from two independent bi-nomial populations. The Z observed was not significant; thus the proportions of students passing for E1 and E2 are not significantly different.

Data obtained on the check ride permitted an analysis among the three groups for four areas: VOR navigation; ADF navigation; VOR, VOR/DME Approach; and NDB Approach. The means for each group for each of the four areas were computed. Visual inspection of the means indicates only minor differences among the means for all of the four variables.

A general linear models procedure was used to compute a MANOVA to determine the significance of the difference among the three groups across the six areas. An exact F-Test based on Wilk's criterion was not significant.

The results of the studies conducted over the four and a half past years indicate that an integrated contact/instrument flight training programme with substantial concentration of instrument procedures at the beginning of training is effective. Conducting the programme over a four semester period is important since the time commitment for the one or the two semester course would be difficult to sustain in a University environment.

It is interesting to note that no significant differences were found between the two experimental groups even though the integrated contact/instrument group (E1) had received substantially more instrument training in the aircraft than E2, the accelerated instrument group (53.1 hours compared to 34.5 hours). The lack of difference may be explained in terms of recency of training, since a substantial part of the additional instrument training for E1 was concentrated during the first two semesters while all of E2's instrument training was during the third and fourth semester.

INTRODUCTION

The Institute of Aviation, University of Illinois conducts a Federal Aviation Administration (FAA) approved flight training programme under Federal Aviation Regulations (FAR Part 141) which consists of a two semester sequence of instruction leading to a Private Pilot certificate. Following Private Pilot certification the Institute conducts an additional four semester sequence which leads to a Commercial Pilot certificate with Instrument rating. During the Private Pilot course student pilots initially are taught to fly using visual cues external to the cockpit (contact flight; also referred to as flight under Visual Flight Rules [VFR]). Although some training is concerned with the use of instruments during this initial phase of pilot training, traditionally contact cues are emphasized and flight solely by reference to instruments (Instrument Flight Rules [IFR]), follows the initial training.

A number of studies and experimental flight training programmes have investigated whether it is more effective to teach contact or instrument flying first (Lee, 1935; Ritchie & Michael, 1955), or to teach an integrated flight training programme (Williams, Houston & Wilkerson, 1956; Easter & Hubbard, 1968). Lee (1935), of the Boeing School of Aeronautics, trained 16 students during their first 23 hours of flight to fly solely by reference to instruments and later trained them using contact cues. The sequence of instruction was so effective that he concluded that '...all students taking instruction for long-time courses, such as our Airline Pilot course (250 hours), should begin their flight instruction under the hood'. This early study did not use control groups nor did it integrate contact and instrument cues during initial training.

In 1955, Ritchie and Michael reported a study in which two groups of subjects were taught to fly straight and level and to make 180° turns. One group was first trained on instruments to a performance criterion; the other group was first trained using contact cues to the same criterion. After reaching the criterion, the training method was switched for each group to determine the amount of transfer from the first training method to the second. For the initial training condition, the contact first group required fewer trials than the instrument first group to reach criterion for both tasks. For the transfer condition, however, the contact to instruments group (contact first group) had a -22 percent transfer while the instrument to contact group (instrument first group) had a +47 percent transfer. Ritchie and Michael (1955) interpreted these results as support for teaching instrument flying prior to teaching contact flying. Williams, Houston, and Wilkerson (1956) conducted an experimental programme that integrated contact and instrument flight training. Eighteen beginning flight students served as subjects in a 35 flight hour Private Pilot syllabus, which included eleven hours of Link instrument training. All students passed the Private Pilot flight check and also demonstrated substantial instrument flight ability, but none qualified for the Instrument rating. Easter and Hubbard (1968) also investigated the concept of an integrated flight training curriculum. This experiment produced a superior private pilot, but failed to produce skills required for the Instrument rating.

The FAA issues Instrument ratings under the Federal Aviation Regulations (FAR) Part 61. In June 1985, the FAA reduced the hours required for an Instrument rating from 200 hours to 125 hours total pilot flight time, 50 hours of which must be as pilot in command (PIC) during cross-country flight (Part FAR 61.65). Subsequently, the Institute of Aviation designed an experimental flight programme which concentrated on teaching instrument skills in an integrated contact/instrument programme.

The study reported by Kaiser, Weinberg, Davis, Benn and Taylor (1986) was completed during one semester and involved 78.6 hours total flight, 34 simulator hours and 90 ground training hours. The objective of the study was to determine whether the six subjects trained in the integrated flight programme would meet the FAA requirements for a Private Pilot certificate with Instrument rating. Four subjects completed the programme; three of these demonstrated the required proficiency for a Private Pilot certificate with Instrument rating and the fourth needed 'a couple of periods of instruction' to correct procedural and control deficiencies.

Taylor, Kaiser, Weinberg and Benn (1987) reported an integrated flight training programme structured to qualify students for the Private Pilot certificate with Instrument rating in two semesters. Thirteen beginning aviation students served as subjects. The syllabus consisted of 105 flight hours, 30 simulator hours and 180 ground training hours. The objective for the first semester was to complete the Private Pilot certificate while integrating substantial instrument training. All 13 subjects successfully completed the first semester training and were awarded the Private Pilot certificate. The objective for the second semester was to complete the Instrument rating. Eleven of the 13 subjects completed the second semester's training. Two students withdrew for reasons not related to the experiment. The eleven students required between 108 and 115 flight hours and between 32 and 40 simulator hours before they were recommended for the Instrument rating check ride. Eight of the eleven subjects qualified for the Instrument rating on the initial check ride. Two subjects qualified for the Instrument rating on the second attempt following minimal additional instruction and one subject was not recommended for a recheck.

The purpose of the present experiment, conducted under an FAA exemption from the flight hour requirement of FAR Part 141, was to replicate systematically the Taylor et al (1987) experiment. The FAA exemption provides for a proficiency-based curriculum. In addition, a second purpose was to compare the integrated contact/instrument programme described by Taylor et al (1987), but conducted over four semesters, with the effectiveness of conducting an accelerated, two semester instrument programme following completion of the Private Pilot certificate under the Institute's regular part 141 training programme. The third purpose was to compare, using selective performance measures, the two groups in the experimental programmes with a control group enrolled in the Institute's regular commercial/instrument training programme.

METHOD

Equipment
Beechcraft Sport and Sundowner aircraft, and Link trainers (GAT-1) and ILLInois Micro Aviation Computer (ILLIMAC) trainers were used. The aircraft have a 180 horsepower engine, fixed gear and a fixed pitch propeller. The ground trainers have navigation and communication equipment required for IFR flight (see Taylor, Staples, Todd & Harshbarger, 1984; Taylor, Hyman, Todd & Hodel, 1985; Kaiser et al, 1986; Taylor et al, 1987; which further describe the ground trainers).

Subjects
A total of thirty-nine Institute of Aviation beginning students served as subjects during the first half of the study (third semester of the four semester test programme sequence). They were divided into three groups as follows: Control group (C), consisting of fifteen subjects enrolled in the FAA approved six semester flight training programme described above (two semester Private Pilot sequence and four semester Commercial/Instrument sequence); Experimental group one (E1), consisting of ten subjects enrolled in an integrated four semester course sequence that contained substantial instrument instruction during the first two semesters leading to Private Pilot certification and concentrated instrument instruction leading to the Instrument rating after the second two semesters; Experimental group two (E2), consisting of fourteen subjects enrolled in the same FAA approved

flight training curriculum as C for the first two semesters (Private Pilot certification) and an accelerated instrument training programme during the second two semesters.

Six subjects failed to enrol during the fourth semester for the second half of the study, for reasons unrelated to the study. Four were members of the C group and two were members of E1. In addition, one subject from E2 was grounded due to an FAA violation on a cross-country flight. Consequently, thirty-two subjects completed the study. For the fourth semester the C group had eleven subjects, the E1 group had eight subjects and the E2 group had thirteen subjects.

Procedures
Experimental Groups. In the fall 1987 semester, the beginning flight students were divided into two groups, C and E1. The control group received a two semester sequence of instruction under the Institute of Aviation Part FAR 141 approved flight training programme leading to Private Pilot certification. These students received 58 flight hours, 12 simulator hours and 90 ground instruction hours. Four of the flight hours consisted of instrument instruction. Following completion of Private Pilot certification, this group was divided into C and E2. The former received the first two semesters of the FAA approved four semester sequence of instruction leading to Commercial Pilot certification with Instrument rating which included 90 hours of ground training. Table 1 contains a summary of the aircraft and simulator hours for the three groups for the four semesters.

After receiving the Private Pilot certificate under the two semester Part FAR 141 approved programme, E2 received an additional two semester experimental programme of accelerated instrument training leading to the Instrument rating. For the third semester, this programme consisted of 20 hours of dual flight instruction, at least 12.6 hours of which were instrument flight instruction (simulated or actual); 18.5 hours of the dual instruction was cross-country pilot-in-command (PIC). In addition, this group received 14 hours of dual instruction in the ground trainer. A total of eleven instrument cross-country flights, which ranged in duration from 1.0 to 3.0 hours, were conducted. Basic attitude instrument flying was introduced in the ground trainer and subsequently practised during cross-country flights. Instrument approach procedures were introduced and extensively practised in the ground trainer and subsequently practised on cross-country flights.

E2 received 45 hours of ground instruction concerned with instrument flight during the third semester. For the fourth semester, E2 received 21.2 hours of dual flight instruction, at least 16.7 hours of which were instrument flight (simulated or actual); 20 hours of the dual instruction were cross-country PIC. In addition, E2 received 12 hours in the ground trainer. A total of eleven instrument cross-country flights, which ranged in duration from 1.0 to 3.0 hours, were conducted. E2 also received an additional 45 hours of ground instruction in instrument procedures during the fourth semester. The purpose of the fourth semester's training was to prepare the student for the Instrument Rating flight check (see areas of evaluation below under fourth semester).

E1 received substantial instrument training during the first two semesters during which they also qualified for Private Pilot certification; they received 90 hours of ground school consisting of contact and instrument instruction. The subjects in E1 received 21 hours of dual instrument instruction in the aircraft during their Private Pilot training, an additional 14 hours during the third semester, and 18.1 hours during the fourth semester for a total of 53.1 hours of instrument flight instruction. They also received 20.5 hours of ground trainer time (14.3 dual and 6.2 solo) during the first two semesters. They received an additional 8 hours of dual ground trainer instruction during the third semester, and 6.8 hours during the fourth semester for a total of 35.3 ground trainer hours. The flight hours and ground school hours during the third semester and fourth semester were essentially the same as those for E2 (see Table 1).

Flight Instructors. The flight instructors from the Institute of Aviation's Pilot Training Department conducted the flight training for all subjects.

Evaluation

Third Semester. Each subject in groups E1 and E2 was given a Basic Instrument Stage Check and was required to complete an IFR cross-country flight. The completion standards required that the student demonstrate the control and accurate manoeuvring of the aircraft solely by reference to instruments for the following areas:

1. Cross-country flying (departure, enroute and arrival);
2. Holding pattern at an intersection;
3. Very high frequency Omni Range (VOR) approach;
4. Instrument Landing System (ILS) approach;
5. Basic instrument airwork;
6. General airmanship.

The expected proficiency standard for heading was plus or minus twenty degrees and for altitude plus or minus one hundred feet. The student was required to demonstrate departure, enroute, arrival and approach procedures to the proficiency level of the Instrument Rating Practical Test Standard (1986) using at least a VOR and an ILS approach.

For group C, each subject was given a Basic Instrument Stage Check comprising: (1) Area departure to a hold; (2) Airwork; and (3) Area arrival and instrument approach.

Two areas of evaluation, airwork and holding pattern, had common tasks that were performed by all three groups. The common tasks evaluated under airwork were: (1) standard rate turns; (2) constant rate climbs; (3)

constant airspeed climbs; (4) level off and level flight; and (5) airspeed and configuration changes. The common tasks under holding pattern were: (1) fix identification; (2) hold entry; and (3) holding pattern sizing and wind correction.

For all three groups, the check pilot was required to complete a standardized stage check form that contained from four to eight tasks for each of the six areas evaluated for E1 and E2 and six to twelve tasks for each of the three areas evaluated for C. The check pilot was required to rate each task on a five point scale as follows: 1 (unsatisfactory) - 5 (excellent). The check pilot was also required to recommend the student for one of the following: (1) continue to the next course; (2) enrol in a remedial course for additional training; (3) retake the stage check; or (4) retake the course.

Fourth Semester. For E1 and E2 the flight check for the completion of the fourth semester was the FAA Instrument Rating Practical Test, and the test format used the FAA Practical Test Standards (1986). The test included cross-country procedures; holding procedures; VOR, ILS, and Non-Directional Beacon (NDB) approaches; Distance Measuring Equipment (DME) arcs; emergency procedures including partial panel procedures (no-gyro); missed approach procedures; circling approaches; and instrument reference manoeuvres. The criteria for all instrument operations were the standards specified in the FAA Practical Test Standards (1986). A rating of unsatisfactory on any task of the Practical Test Standards results in the student failing the check ride. All E1 and E2 students were expected to take the Instrument flight test when they reached the required proficiency and were recommended by their flight instructors.

The following six major areas were evaluated for E1 and E2:
1. Ground Phase – 5 tasks;
2. Air Traffic Control Clearances and Procedures – 3 tasks;
3. Flight by Reference to Instruments – 7 tasks;
4. Navigation Aids – 2 tasks;
5. No-Gyro Procedures – 1 task;
6. Instrument Approach Procedures – 6 tasks.

The control group was evaluated on a stage check concerned with IFR navigation and approaches and comprising the following four areas: (1) Pre-flight operations; (2) IFR navigation (pre-flight and in-flight computations, VOR navigation, ADF navigation); (3) Instrument approaches; and (4) Miscellaneous.

Four areas of evaluation (VOR navigation, Automatic Direction Finding [ADF] navigation, VOR and VOR/DME approach and NDB approach) had common tasks that were performed by all three groups. These common tasks were evaluated to compare the two experimental groups with the control group. The check pilot was required to complete a standardized check ride form as described above which consisted of a five point rating scale. In addition, the check pilot was required to provide an overall rating of the student's performance using a five point scale. The check pilot was also required to recommend each student for one of the following: (1) continue to the next course; (2) enrol in a remedial course for additional training; (3) retake the stage check; or (4) retake the course. One check pilot conducted all instrument checks for E1 and E2 and the stage checks for the control group.

RESULTS

Semester 3

All students in the three groups with the exception of one in group E2 successfully completed the stage check and were recommended to take the next course sequence. The unsuccessful student received 1.5 aircraft hours and one simulator hour of remedial training and subsequently successfully completed the stage check.

The rating scores for all tasks in each of the six areas were summed and mean scores were computed for each area for groups E1 and E2; a mean total score was also computed. The means for E1 and E2 for each area of evaluation are shown in Figure 1. Inspection of the means indicates only minor differences between the means of the two experimental groups for any of the areas of evaluation.

A general linear models procedure was used to compute a multi-variate analysis of variance (MANOVA) to determine the significance between the two groups for the six areas of evaluation. There were 24 observations in the data set and there were two missing values. Thus only 22 observations were used for the MANOVA. An exact F-Test, based on Wilk's criterion, was used to test the differences between the two groups; the results were $F_{(6, 15)} = 0.64$, $p < 0.69$, indicating no significant difference between the two groups across the six areas of evaluation. Uni-variate analyses of variance (ANOVAs) were computed using the general linear models procedure for each of the six areas of evaluation to test the significance of the difference between the two experimental groups (E1 and E2) for each area of evaluation. No significant differences were found for any of the areas of evaluation.

Data obtained on the stage check permitted an analysis among the three groups for airwork and holding. The means of the three groups for the two instrument tasks are shown in Figure 2. A general linear models procedure was used to compute F-Tests to test the significance of the difference between the means. No significant difference was found for airwork but an F-Test for the main effect of holding was significant ($F_{[2, 35]} = 3.46$, $p < 0.04$). Linear contrasts indicated that the significance was due to differences between the control group and E2.

Table 1. Summary of aircraft and simulator hours

	Dual	Solo	Total XC	GT Dual/ Solo	SI	PIC	PIC* X-C
E1							
Semester 1	24.1	2.0	9.1	14.3	10.0	-	-
Semester 2	20.0	12.0	20.6	6.2	11.0	-	-
Sub-Total***	44.1	14.0	29.7	20.5	21.0	-	-
Semester 3	20.2	7.8	23.6	8.0	14.0	28.0	17.6
Semester4	21.2	5.4	26.6	6.8	18.1	8.4	21.2
Sub-Total	41.4	13.2	50.2	14.8	32.1	56.4	38.8
Total	85.5	27.8	79.9	35.3	53.1	56.4	38.8
E2							
Semester 1	21.0	3.0	-	4/2	2.0	-	-
Semester 2	19.0	12.0	15.0	4/2	2.0	-	-
Sub-Total***	40.0	15.0	15.0	8/4	4.0	-	-
Semester 3	20.0	6.5	24.5	14.0	13.8	28.0	18.5
Semester 4	21.2	6.0	26.0	12.0	16.7	28.7	20.0
Sub-Total****	41.2	12.5	50.5	26.0	30.5	56.7	36.5
Total	81.2	27.5	65.5	38.0	34.5	56.7	36.5
Control (C)							
Semester 1	21.0	3.0	-	4/2	2.0	-	-
Semester 2	19.0	12.0	15.0	4/2	2.0	-	-
Sub-Total***	40.0	15.0	15.0	8/4	4.0	-	-
Semester 3	15.0	12.0	7.5	6/2	9.5	20.5	-
Semester 4	16.0	12.0	6.0	4/4	9.5	16.5	-
Sub-Total	31.0	24.0	13.5	10/6	19.0	36.5	-
Total	71.0	39.0	28.5	18/10	23.0	36.5	-

* Flight Instructor on Board; ** Check Pilot;
*** Private Pilot Certification; **** Instrument Rating

Semester 4

Nine of eleven students in the control group successfully completed the stage check on the first attempt and were recommended to take the next course in the four course commercial/instrument sequence. The two students

Table 1 (continued).

	Solo XC	Total Night	Night X-C	Night X-C PIC	PIC** Stage Check	CUM Hours
E1						
	-	-	-	-	-	27.1
	10.0	1.5	1.5	-	-	34.0
	10.0	1.5	-	-	61.1	81.1
	6.0	2.2	2.2	2.2	1.5	28.0
	5.4	3.2	3.2	3.2	1.8	28.4
	11.4	5.4	5.4	5.4	3.3	56.4
	21.4	6.9	6.9	3.4	3.3	117.5
E2						
	-	1	-	-	-	25
	10.0	2	1	-	-	33
	10.0	3	1	-	-	58
	6.0	2.5	2.5	2.5	1.5	28.0
	6.0	3.0	3.0	3.0	1.5	28.7
	12.0	5.5	5.5	5.5	3.0	56.7
	22.0	8.5	6.5	5.5	3.0	114.7
Control (C)						
	-	1	-	-	-	25
	10.0	2	1	-	-	33
	10.0	3	1	-	-	58
	6.0	-	-	-	1.0	28
	6.0	-	-	-	1.0	28
	12.0	-	-	-	2.0	56
	22.0	3	1	-	2.0	114

XC = Cross-country; GT = Ground Trainer;
SI = Simulated Instrument; PIC = Pilot in Command

who failed the initial stage passed the recheck satisfactorily and were recommended to proceed to the next course.

For E1, six of the eight students successfully completed the check ride for the Instrument rating. The two students who failed the initial Instrument rating check ride passed the recheck. Two of thirteen of the students in E2 were not recommended for the Instrument rating but were given the check ride. In addition to these two, four additional students (six total) failed to complete the check ride successfully for the Instrument rating on the first attempt, while seven passed on the first try. Three of the four passed the recheck while the fourth student required two rechecks before successfully completing the check ride.

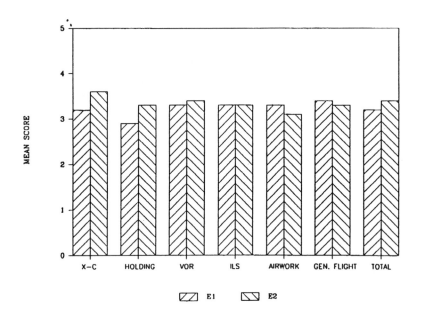

Figure 1. Means of the areas of evaluation

A 2 x 3 Chi-square was computed to test the significance of the difference among the number of passes for the three groups.

The Chi-square with DF = 2 using Yates's correction resulted in X = 2.36, p < 0.31, indicating that the number of students passing on the first attempt among the three groups was not significant.

The rating scores for all tasks in each of the six areas of the Instrument Rating Practical Test Standards were summed and mean scores were computed for each area for groups E1 and E2. A mean total score was also computed. There were three missing values for the No-Gyro Procedures. The mean score for each group for the No-Gyro Procedures was used to estimate the value of the missing score(s) for that group. The means for E1 and E2 for each area of the Instrument Rating Practical Test Standards are shown in Figure 3. Inspection indicates only minor differences between the means of the two experimental groups for any of the areas.

A general linear models procedure was used to compute a MANOVA to test the significance of the difference between the two groups for the six areas of the Instrument Rating Practical Test Standards. There were 21 observations in the data set and three missing values (all for the No-Gyro Procedures); thus only 18 observations were used to compute the MANOVA. An exact F-Test based on Wilk's criterion resulted in $F(6, 11) = 0.40$, $p < 0.862$, which indicated no significant difference between the two groups across the six areas. The general linear models procedure was also used to compute ANOVAs for each of the six areas to test the significance of the difference between the two groups (E1 and E2) on each of the areas. None of the F-Tests for the six areas indicates a significant difference between the two groups (E1 and E2).

A 2 x 2 Chi-square was computed to test the significance of the difference between the number of subjects who passed the Instrument rating check ride on the first attempt for E1 and E2. The Chi-square with DF = 1 using Yates's correction resulted in $X = 0.26$, $p < 0.61$. Thus, no significant difference between the number of subjects in E1 and E2 who passed the Instrument rating flight check was found.

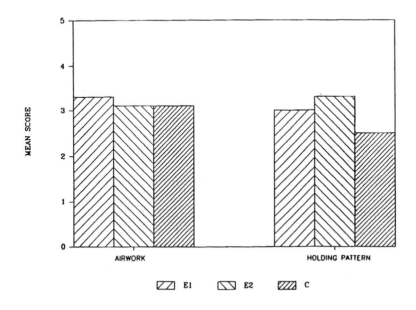

Figure 2. Means of instrument tasks

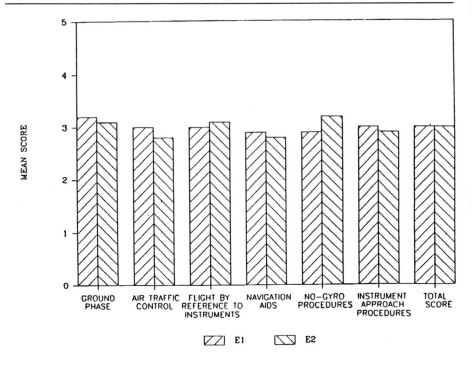

Figure 3. Means of the areas of the instrument
rating practical test guide

Since three of four of the cells of the Chi-square had an N of 5 or less, a Z statistic was computed to determine whether the numbers of subjects in E1 and E2 passing the Instrument rating check ride were from two independent bi-nomial populations. The result (Z observed = 1.025; p[Z > 1.025] = 0.15390) indicated no significant difference between E1 and E2 in the number of students passing.

Data obtained on the check ride permitted an analysis among the three groups for four areas: VOR navigation; ADF navigation; VOR, VOR/DME Approach; and NDB Approach. There was a significant amount of missing data, particularly for the Control group for ADF navigation and NDB approach. The mean for each group for each of the four areas was used to estimate the missing value in order to compute the means. The means for the three groups for these four variables are shown in Figure 4. Visual inspection of the means indicate only minor differences among the means for all of the four variables.

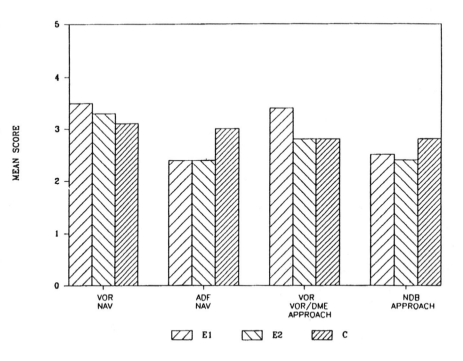

Figure 4. Means of instrument navigation and approaches

A general linear models procedure was used to compute a MANOVA to determine the significance of the difference among the three groups across the four areas. There were 32 observations in the data set but no observations with missing values were used. Thus only 20 observations were used in the analysis. An exact F-Test based on Wilk's criterion resulted in F $(8, 28) = 0.55$, p < 0.81.

It should be noted that the partial correlation coefficient from the error matrix for ADF navigation and NDB approach indicated that r = .91, p < 0.001; and the correlation for VOR navigation and VOR, VOR/DME indicated that r = .62, p > 0.006. Thus, the VOR navigation and approach were measuring the same skills and the ADF navigation and NDB approach were measuring the same population of skills. ANOVAs were computed for each of the four areas and no significant differences among the three groups were found for any of the areas.

DISCUSSION

The results of the current study systematically replicated the findings of Taylor et al (1987) and Kaiser et al (1986) that an integrated contact/instrument flight training programme with substantial concentration of instrument procedures at the beginning of training is effective. Conducting the programme over a four semester period is important since the time commitment for the one or the two semester course would be difficult to sustain in a University environment. There is evidence from Kaiser et al (1986), however, that the concentrated one semester course using an integrated flight training programme may be more effective than either the two or four semester course sequence of the present study (Taylor et al, 1987) semester course. As previously noted, the concentrated course is difficult to maintain in a University flight training environment.

It is interesting to note that no significant differences were found between the two experimental groups even though the integrated contact/instrument group (E1) had received substantially more instrument training in the aircraft than E2, the accelerated instrument group (53.1 hours compared to 34.5 hours). The lack of difference may be explained in terms of recency of training since a substantial part of the additional instrument training for E1 was concentrated during the first two semesters while all of E2's instrument training was during the third and fourth semesters.

The results of the holding pattern were unexpected. Group E2 performed significantly better on this task than group C even though holding was emphasized during the third semester instrument instruction for group C. Two subjects in group C were unsatisfactory on holding and four were rated below average, whereas only one subject in group E2 was rated below average. The experience of E2 of holding at a variety of different airports, while C's training was limited to the local area, may explain the difference.

Childs (1986) reviewed the relevant military aviation research on integrated flight training. He concluded that the available data, most of which were collected during the 1950s and 1960s, largely supported the feasibility of providing beginning flight students with instrument training during the early phases of flight training. He concluded that there is little doubt that instrument instruction during early training can be beneficial. Our previous studies as well as the current study support this conclusion but the question of the amount of instrument instruction to be integrated with contact instruction remains unanswered. Our study indicates that concentrated instrument training following largely contact instruction to Private Pilot certification works as well as the more substantial integration of instrument instruction during the contact phase. Based on current estimates, it appears that our students will be able to obtain a commercial certificate with one additional semester's training following completion of the Private Pilot certificate with Instrument Rating, thus saving one semester of training time and cost.

The high transfer from instrument training to contact flight reported by Ritchie and Michael (1955) and Kaiser et al (1986) indicates that integrating instrument training should reduce hazards of contact flight. Since instrument skills can be acquired in a ground trainer, safety can be further improved.

The question of the effectiveness of ground trainers and flight simulators for flight training is no longer in doubt. Orlansky and String (1977) reviewed 33 research studies conducted between 1939 and 1977; these studies showed that flight simulators are effective for training purposes. They concluded that training in simulators reduces the time needed to acquire the same skills in aircraft; they also concluded that flight simulators are most effective for training on tasks that involve following precise procedures such as in instrument flight and approach and landing.

Based on the results of the calculations of transfer effectiveness, Orlansky and String (1977) concluded that simulators are effective for training. With few exceptions, when comparing the experimental group to the control group, training time in the simulator saved training time in the aircraft. Transfer effectiveness ratios ranged from -0.4 to 1.9 with a median value of 0.45. The effectiveness of simulators varied widely across the different studies, but the median values indicated positive transfer. The median transfer effectiveness ratio, the most common measure of effectiveness currently in use, indicates that almost half an hour of flight time was saved for each hour in the simulator.

Indeed the use of ground trainers that are less costly to operate than aircraft provides additional advantages. This is particularly important for military flight training. As Blaiwes, Puig and Regan (1973) point out, the task of determining the effectiveness of a simulator does not end with a transfer of training study. In order to address cost-effectiveness issues in flight simulation, operating cost ratios for simulators and aircraft have to be compared.

Orlansky and String (1977) computed, from United States Air Force, Army, and Navy, and commercial airline data sources, cost ratios for the variable operating costs of 33 pairs of simulators and aircraft. The ratios ranged from 0.02 to 0.40 with a median ratio of 0.11. Orlansky, Knapp and String (1984) analysed the variable operating costs for 39 United States military aircraft and their respective flight simulators for fiscal years 1980 and 1981. The operating costs for the flight simulators ranged between $37 and $322 per hour while the operating costs for the aircraft ranged from $211 to $6420 per hour. The median simulator/aircraft operating cost ratio percentage for the 39 simulators/aircraft was 8 percent – the same ratio percentage reported by Orlansky and String (1977) for 17 pairs of military aircraft.

It has been demonstrated that integrated flight training is effective; that instrument training in training devices and simulators is effective; and that the operating costs of simulators are substantially less for those devices than for aircraft.

REFERENCES

Blaiwes, A.A., Puig, J.A., and Regan, J.J. (1973). Transfer of training and the measurement of training effectiveness. *Human Factors,* 15, 523-533.

Childs, J.M. (1986). Integrated flight training. *Human Factors,* 28, 559-565.

Easter, M. and Hubbard, W. (1968). *Experimental Training Program Utilizing an Integrated VFR-IFR Curriculum.* Department of Aviation, Ohio State University, Columbus, Ohio.

Federal Aviation Administration (1986). *Instrument Rating Practical Test Standards.* FAA-S-8081-4.

Kaiser, R.H. (1986). *Century Program II: IFR-VFR Teaching Method.* Pilot training, Institute of Aviation, University of Illinois, Savoy, Illinois.

Kaiser, R.H., Weinberg, R.A., Davis, T. Jr., Benn, O., and Taylor, H.L. (1986). *A combined instrument/private pilot flight training program.* Proceedings of the IEEE National Aerospace and Electronics Conference – NAECON (pp.1040-1047), Dayton, Ohio.

Lee, T. Jr. (1935). Instrument flying from scratch. *Aviation,* 34, December, 1935. Secondary Reference in Williams, Houston & Wilkerson (1956).

Orlansky, J., Knapp, M.I., and String, J. (1984). *Operating Costs of Aircraft and Flight Simulators.* IDA Paper P-1733. Alexandria, VA: Institute for Defense Analysis.

Orlansky, J. and String, J. (1977). *Cost-Effectiveness of Flight Simulators for Military Training. Vol. 1: Use and Effectiveness of Flight Simulators.* IDA Paper No. P-1275, Arlington, VA: Institute for Defense Analysis.

Ritchie, M.L. and Michael, A.L. (1955). Transfer between instrument and contact flight. *Journal of Applied Psychology,* 39, 145-149.

Taylor, H.L., Staples, L.A., Todd, R.E., and Harshbarger, T.L. (1984). The ILLInois Microcomputer Aviation Computer (ILLIMAC) simulator. *Proceedings of the IEEE National Aerospace and Electronics Conference – NAECON* pp. 1016- 1023, Dayton, Ohio.

Taylor, H.L., Hyman, F.C., Todd, R.E., and Hodel, A.S. (1985). Instructor station for the ILLIMAC general aviation instrument training simulator. *Proceedings of the IEEE National Aerospace and Electronics Conference – NAECON,* pp. 1111-1118.

Taylor, H.L., Kaiser, R.H., Weinberg, R.A., and Benn, O. (1987). An integrated instrument/private pilot flight training program. *Proceedings of the Fourth International Symposium on Aviation Psychology,* pp. 515-521.

Williams, A.C. Jr., Houston, R.C., and Wilkerson, L.E. (1956). Simultaneous contact-instrument flight training. *Aeronautics Bulletin* No. 18, University of Illinois Bulletin, 53.

ACKNOWLEDGEMENTS

The authors thank the Institute of Aviation students, and flight instructors, who participated in the study. Mr Steve Owen deserves special recognition for conducting the final check rides. We wish to express our appreciation to Ms Lynn Chung and Ms Suna Barlas for conducting the statistical analysis and to Dr Martha Weller for constructing the graphic materials. We also wish to thank Mrs Diana Christenson and Mrs Sharon Allen for preparing the manuscript.

17

A conceptualization of aviation psychology on the civil flight deck

John B. Long

ABSTRACT

This paper proposes a conceptualization of aviation psychology on the flight deck of passenger transport aircraft. Such a conceptualization is needed to relate: (i) topics within the 'operational issues' section of this volume; (ii) other topic sections within Volumes I and II; and (iii) topics outside these volumes. It is based on conceptions for an engineering discipline of human factors (Dowell & Long, 1989) and for the discipline of human-computer interaction (Long & Dowell, 1989), and expresses the flight deck and the aircrew as an interactive worksystem for flying aircraft, as it supports the transportation of air passengers. The design of the crew's interaction with the flight deck constitutes the general problem for aviation psychology practice as supported by aviation psychology knowledge. The conceptualization is illustrated by means of topics taken from this volume and from elsewhere. The paper offers a modest contribution to the development of a consensus view of applied aviation psychology on the flight deck, and a general consensus view of work and worksystems.

INTRODUCTION

The flight deck is an example of technology at work. The aircrew of a passenger aircraft interacts with the flightdeck to operate and to control the aircraft, such as to ensure, for example, the 'safe and expeditious transportation of passengers from one location to another'. As with other examples of technology at work, the interaction of the crew with the flight deck is designed on the basis of specialist knowledge which supports that design practice. The question arises as to how the interaction between the crew and the flight deck should be conceptualized with respect to specialist knowledge and practice, and in particular the specialist knowledge and practice of aviation psychology.

This paper proposes such a conceptualization based on a conception for the discipline of human factors, and a framework for conceptions of the discipline of human-computer interaction. For present purposes, the flight deck will be considered as the workplace of the crew of passenger transport aircraft. Other flight deck environments (e.g. combat/defence aircraft) are beyond the scope of the present conceptualization, since their occupants are engaged in work of a different nature. The paper attempts to contribute to the development of a consensus view of aviation psychology on the flight deck, relating explicitly topics that might otherwise be related only implicitly.

REQUIREMENTS FOR A CONCEPTUALIZATION

The requirements for a conceptualization of aviation psychology on the flight deck, as they relate to this paper, include specific, general, and novel concerns.

The specific concerns are those addressed by the contributions to this section. There are three such contributions. Dale reports on the results of a questionnaire survey concerning a no smoking trial on military charter flights between the United Kingdom and Germany or Gibraltar. The survey was intended to investigate passenger attitudes towards the smoking ban; passenger opinions on the effectiveness of different strategies to reduce non-smoker discomfort; and the propensity of passengers to smoke immediately before and during the flight. Taylor et al report on the effectiveness of three types of training programme for private pilots: (i) an integrated contact (that is using visual reference to the ground) plus instrument programme; (ii) an accelerated instrument programme; and (iii) a standard private pilot plus commercial/instrument programme. Selcon et al provide an account of the decrease in choice response time resulting from redundant display information on the basis of experiments concerning the use of feedback in direct voice input; the perception of words with shared semantics; and the reaction to warning icons. A conceptualization is required if these apparently disparate topics are to be related in a coherent manner.

The general concerns requiring conceptualization include those topic categories addressed in the remaining sections of these volumes, including: stress and error; selection and training; simulation; sleep management; and accidents.

Lastly, novel concerns requiring conceptualization include new approaches to the design of the flight deck, such as the concept of the 'electronic crewmember', based on knowledge-based systems technology, to support the pilot in carrying out his/her activities; the provision of in-flight interactive terminals to passengers for electronic shopping, banking, and communication; and the proposed use of pilots, travelling as passengers, to help the aircrew in cases of emergency. A conceptualization is also needed to relate these novel concerns to one another, as well as to the specific and general concerns of aviation psychology on the flight deck.

CONCEPTUALIZATION

The conceptualization comprises an expression of the flight deck appropriate for the concerns of aviation psychology, and an expression of aviation psychology appropriate for the concerns of the flight deck. The former is based on an engineering conception for human factors proposed by Dowell and Long (1989), and the latter on a framework for conceptions of human-computer interaction proposed by Long and Dowell (1989). Taken together, the conceptualization supports the relations between specific, general, and novel issues discussed above.

Following Dowell and Long (1989), the flight deck and aircrew are conceptualized as an interactive worksystem comprising two behavioural sub-systems. One is the flight deck behaviours as expressed by flight deck devices (instruments and controls, etc.); the other is the aircrew behaviours as expressed by aircrew members (captain, first officer, etc.). The interaction of these two behavioural sub-systems constitutes the interactive flightsystem.

The interactive flightsystem is be to distinguished from the work it performs, that is transporting passengers from one location to another by air. Hence, the work of flying aircraft originates, is performed, and has its consequences in the domain of air passenger transportation, which intersects air passenger transportation organizations (civil and military) with air passenger transportation technology (aircraft, radar, etc.). Flying aircraft thus represents part of the work that more generally constitutes air passenger transportation. An interactive flightsystem carries out the work of transporting passengers by operating and controlling the aircraft.

Transporting passengers by air is conceptualized as effecting changes in the 'objects' comprising the application domain of the flight system, that is the passengers. Passengers are both abstract and physical, and are characterized by attributes having states. Such passenger attributes include: location (London, Beijing); safety (injured, uninjured); satisfaction (pleased, displeased); etc. The product goal of the flightsystem's transportation of the passengers is specified as a desired transformation of the passengers, for example, their location at Beijing (from London); safe (uninjured by the flight); and satisfied (pleased by the flight). The interactive flightsystem transports passengers in an attempt to achieve this product goal. This expression of the product goal is at a high level of description. The goal is re-expressible at a lower level as task goals, for example, as flying a particular flight course at a particular speed and height, such as to avoid other aircraft, to minimize flying time or fuel consumption, and to avoid turbulent atmospheric conditions likely to discomfort passengers.

The behaviours of the interactive flightsystem committed to achieving this product goal are supported by two independent structures or sets of structures – the aircrew (comprising mental and physical structures) and the flight deck devices (comprising informational and physical structures). Note that the structures of the two sub-systems (for example, the pilot's mental representation of the terrain and the flight deck's representation stored in the computer) do not interact directly, but only through the behaviours they support – the pilot's strategic scanning (behaviour) of the computer's terrain map display (behaviour).

In attempting to achieve the product goal, the interactive flightsystem is to be conceptualized as incurring resource costs. Aircrew and flight deck devices alike incur such costs, both structural and behavioural. The structural costs of the aircrew include the cost of acquiring flying skills and expertise, including the experience required for strategic scanning of terrain displays. The structural costs of a flight deck computer include the cost of developing the software required to display the terrain map (for it to be strategically scanned by the aircrew). The behavioural costs of the interactive flight system are those incurred in transporting passengers. They are incurred by the aircrew in the strategic scanning of the display and by the flight deck computer in the displaying of the terrain map. Both the structural and behavioural resource costs of the aircrew are to be conceptualized as cognitive (the extent of knowledge required in the acquisition of strategic scanning skill and in the expression of the scanning behaviour it supports); conative (the extent of effort required in the acquisition of the skill and its use); and affective (the extent of emotion associated with the acquisition of the skill and its use).

The success with which the interactive flightsystem achieves its product goal of transporting passengers is conceptualized in terms of quality. The performance of the flightsystem expresses the quality achieved and the resource costs incurred, both structural and behavioural, in flying the passengers; it is determined by the interactive behaviours of aircrew and flight deck devices. Desired performance, expressed in terms of the goal of transporting passengers and acceptable resource costs, may differ from actual performance. Reduction of the discrepancy can be achieved by optimizing the interaction of aircrew and flight deck device behaviours.

The conceptualization of the interactive flightsystem, comprising aircrew and flight deck devices; the domain of transporting passengers by air; and the performance with which the system flies the passengers, is now complete. It constitutes an expression of the flight deck appropriate for the concerns of aviation psychology.

The second part of the conceptualization follows: the expression of aviation psychology appropriate for the concerns of the flight deck, conceived as part of the interactive flightsystem transporting passengers by air effectively. The concerns are assumed to relate to the design of the aircrew's interactions with flight deck devices (e.g. strategic scanning of a terrain map displayed by a flight deck computer, as well as a more general explanation and prediction of strategic scanning behaviours). Following

Long and Dowell (1989), a discipline is conceived as the use of knowledge to support practices seeking solutions to a general problem having a particular scope. If the general problem of aviation psychology is ultimately one of design, then the particular scope is to be conceptualized as the design of the aircrew's interaction with the flight deck's devices to transport passengers effectively (and involving strategic scanning rather than simply observing the display). As science includes behavioural science, which includes psychology, which includes aviation psychology, the last is conceptualized as the knowledge indirectly supporting the design of aircrew interactions with flight deck devices. As the knowledge of aviation psychology is, however, purely explanatory and predictive, aviation psychology is re-conceptualized more generally as applied aviation psychology, and the knowledge of aviation psychology must be transformed to the prescriptions required to support design. The transformation may be carried out by the designer and so remain implicit in the designed interaction, or by the researcher or the developer and be expressed explicitly, for example, in the form of design guidelines. Applied aviation psychology, then, which supports the design of interactive flight systems comprises aviation psychology and design guidelines.

The design practices of applied aviation psychology are conceptualized as 'specify the aircrew interaction' (using guidelines based on aviation psychology knowledge), 'implement the interaction' (for example, in a simulated flight deck), and 'test the interaction' (for example, to establish whether desired performance is achieved). Suppose, for example, that aviation psychology established that pilots' scanning behaviour deteriorated (in terms of the time taken to scan and the number of errors committed) as a function of the level of detail displayed by terrain maps, and explained the phenomenon, perhaps in terms of a theory of visual search. The following guideline might then be derived: 'if pilots are required to scan strategically, then reduce the amount of detail displayed by the terrain map'. In the design of a particular flight deck, the application of the guideline might result in the provision of two versions of the terrain map, one with fewer details to be used for strategic scanning and one with more details to be used for other types of scanning. It would be expected that strategic scanning of the terrain map with fewer details would result in faster, strategic scanning with fewer errors. The support of more efficient strategic scanning by a less detailed terrain map would be expected to contribute generally to the success with which the interactive flightsystem transports the passengers.

This (hypothetical) example illustrates how applied aviation psychology knowledge, including design guidelines, might support the practice of designing interactive flightsystems. The conceptualization of aviation psychology, as an applied discipline comprising knowledge, and practices seeking the solution to a general problem having the particular scope of designing the aircrew's interaction with the flight deck's devices to transport passengers effectively, is now complete. It constitutes an expression of aviation psychology appropriate for the concerns of the flight deck.

APPLICATION OF THE CONCEPTUALIZATION

The conceptualization will now be applied to the specific topics in this section; to the general topics in the remaining sections; and to other novel topics (as identified earlier). The application is intended to relate the topics in terms both of its expression of the flight deck and of its expression of aviation psychology. The relations exposed by the conceptualization will be contrasted with relations that might otherwise be supposed (by other conceptualizations).

The three topics addressed in this section are: air passengers' attitudes to a no smoking trial; alternative training programmes for private pilots; and the effects on reaction time of redundant display information. Each will be conceptualized in turn.

In terms of the flight deck, Dale's survey involving a no smoking trial on charter flights is to be conceptualized as a concern with the effectiveness of a particular class of interactive flightsystems – those involved in Ministry of Defence charter flights. The survey is intended to quantify the effects of smoking on passenger 'comfort' and 'safety', both of which refer to the applications domain of the flightsystem. These passenger attributes as they relate to smoking, and so also to the effects of a no smoking trial, are both abstract (approving, disapproving) and physical (irritated throat, non-irritated throat). Values of these attributes (very disapproving, very irritated throat) are presumed to express, at least in part, a possible task goal of the flightsystems and so their desired performance. In terms of aviation psychology, the survey is to be conceptualized as part of (re)design practice attempting to measure actual as opposed to desired performance. A discrepancy might lead to the application of applied aviation psychology knowledge to support the elimination of the discrepancy, for example, by continuing the no smoking ban. The survey might also be conceptualized as an initial attempt to identify air passenger phenomena expressed in terms of their attitudes and activities (smoking before and during the flight) with a view to their subsequent explanation by aviation psychology. The knowledge might be expected to lead to guidelines which in turn might be expected to support (re)design practice. However, the survey as reported essentially constitutes part of (re)design practice as conceptualized in terms of applied aviation psychology.

In terms of the flight deck, Taylor et al's evaluation of three types of training programme for private pilots is to be conceptualized as a concern with the optimization of structural resource costs for the aircrew component of the flightsystem. A training programme that reduces the structural resource costs of acquiring private pilot skills, with no increase in the behavioural cost associated with their use in flying, and with no change in the effectiveness with which passengers are transported, would constitute an optimization. In terms of aviation psychology, the evaluation is to be conceptualized as an assessment of alternative forms of practice, which contribute to the design of pilots' interactions with the flight deck by setting up those structures, in terms of skill and expertise, that support pilot behaviour. Guidelines expressing aviation psychology knowledge might inform the different training programmes. The resulting pilot behaviour might be explained by aviation psychology knowledge. However, the evaluation as reported essentially addresses the issue of alternative forms of practice, as conceptualized in terms of applied aviation psychology.

In terms of the flight deck, Selcon et al's account of the effects on reaction time of redundant display information is to be conceptualized as a concern with the optimization of aircrew behaviour by means of optimizing flight deck device behaviour. Adding redundant information to displays is shown to decrease reaction time. The decrease is achieved at some increased structural and behavioural cost to the flight deck device (in the provision of the redundant information) and possibly also to the operators of the devices. The optimization of aircrew behaviour may be conceptualized as contributing to enhanced flightsystem performance. In terms of aviation psychology, the development of the account of the effects on reaction time of redundant display information, including experimental results and a cognitive model, is to be understood as the acquisition of knowledge that might be expected to explain the phenomena associated with redundant information, and to lead to design guidelines that in turn would be expected to support the practice of designing interactions between aircrew and flight deck devices embodying redundant information. However, the account as reported essentially addresses the acquisition of aviation psychology knowledge concerning the effects on reaction time of redundant display information as conceptualized in terms of applied aviation psychology.

This completes the conceptualization of the specific topics addressed in the present section of this volume. The relations exposed by the conceptualization contrast with those implied by other approaches. For example, a conceptualization in terms of efficiency and well-being would characterize both training programmes and redundant information as a direct contribution to efficiency, and a no smoking trial to well-being. Alternatively, a conceptualization in terms of functionality, usability and acceptability would characterize training programmes as a contribution to usability, redundant information to functionality, and a no smoking trial to acceptability. In contrast, in terms of the approach proposed here, a no smoking trial is assumed to affect task quality; alternative training programmes to affect structural resource costs of the aircrew; and redundant information to affect flight deck resource costs and optimization of aircrew behaviour.

Further contrasts are provided by a conceptualization of aviation psychology as only craft knowledge or as only scientific knowledge (as opposed to applied scientific knowledge). Were aviation psychology to be only craft or scientific knowledge, the no smoking trial survey and the evaluation of alternative pilot training programmes could concern only (re)design practice. The phenomena they identify would not require scientific explanation and there would be no resultant guidelines to support future (re)design practice. The account of redundant display information could not be expressed as guidelines and so would not support (re)design practice. In contrast, in terms of the conceptualization presented here, the no smoking trial survey and the evaluation of alternative private pilot training programmes essentially address issues of (re)design practice (with a potential for scientific explanation and guideline derivation). The account of redundant display information, however, with its cognitive model and laboratory experiments, essentially addresses the acquisition of aviation psychology knowledge (with a potential for guideline derivation and (re)design practice support).

Consideration is now given to the general concerns addressed in the remaining topic sections of Volumes I and II: stress and error; selection and training; simulation; sleep management; and accidents. Each will be conceptualized in turn.

In terms of the flight deck, stress and error are to be conceptualized, respectively, as an inappropriate level of pilot behavioural resource costs, and sub-optimal behaviour(s). Alternatively, stress is to be conceptualized as a passenger attribute that could be used to specify, in part, the task goal of air passenger transport (stressed, unstressed), and so the effectiveness of the flightsystem.

Selection and training are to be conceptualized as alternative (or complementary) approaches to the issue of pilot structural resource costs. In the former case, pilots with the appropriate flying skills and expertise would be selected (so requiring little or no training). In the latter case (in the absence of selection for flying skills), pilots would need to acquire all the skills from their training. Resource costs during training, then, would be expected to differ in the two cases, being greater for the 'unselected' pilots.

Simulation is to be conceptualized as a method (or set of methods) that can be used to aid the acquisition of aviation psychology knowledge, the evaluation of design guidelines derived from that knowledge, and the support of (re)design practice. As such, the method(s) may involve simulation of: the interactive flightsystem (including the aircrew and flight deck); the domain of application of the system, that is the transport of passengers by air; and the effectiveness with which the flightsystem transports the passengers.

Sleep management as it relates to aircrew is to be conceptualized as an 'off-line' task (one not supported by the interactive flight system for transporting passengers) in contrast to an 'on-line' task (one such as strategic scanning that is supported by the flightsystem). The off-line task of sleep management, however, would be expected to have consequences for the aircrew and its behaviour(s). The consequences are to be conceptualized as maintenance of aircrew structures (both physical and mental), such that they be able to support optimal flying behaviours or behaviours required to achieve flightsystem effectiveness. Without appropriate maintenance, air-crew physical and mental structures will support behaviour requiring an unacceptable level of aircrew resource costs and resulting in an undesired level of task quality, perhaps in the form of 'near misses', resulting from a misreading of the instruments, that constitute a failure to achieve the task goal of safe passenger transportation. Alternatively, sleep management as applied to the passengers is to be conceptualized as an attribute (rested, not rested) and as such might or might not be included in the flightsystem's task goals.

Lastly, accidents as they relate to aircraft are to be conceptualized as the flightsystem's failure to conform to task goals and so to achieve desired performance. Accidents are incommensurate with the safe transportation of air passengers, thus indicting the effectiveness of the flightsystem. Accidents indicate that actual flight system performance is failing to achieve desired performance and so demand changes in the flight system's behaviour(s) towards optimization.

In terms of aviation psychology, the general concerns of these volumes discussed above are to be conceptualized in terms of an applied discipline. Simulation is a method (or methods) supporting (re)design and the acquisition of knowledge. The remaining general concerns may be concep-tualized either in terms of the practice of (re)design, of the derivation of guidelines, or of the acquisition of knowledge. This completes the conceptualization of the general concerns of these volumes.

As with the conceptualization of the flight deck topics, the relations exposed between the general concerns differ from those supposed by other conceptualizations. For example, an alternative approach in terms of efficiency and well-being would characterize stress (and error) and sleep management as concerning not only the efficiency of the aircrew, but the well-being of both the aircrew and the passengers. A common source of stress, such as excessively dry air, might be assumed to affect the well-being of both aircrew and passengers, and a common (re)design solution sought. The distinction between dry air as a determinant of increased aircrew behavioural resource costs (which might or might not be associated with a decrease in task quality, for example, safe transportation of passengers) and dry air as a determinant of a change in passenger attributes (dry throat, moist throat; displeased, pleased) would be lost (and so perhaps the need for a differential solution to the problem of excessively dry air). Alternatively, a flight deck conceptualized in terms of functionality, usability and acceptabi-lity would characterize dry air as a source of stress affecting both the aircrew and the passengers, with respect to the flight deck and the cabin respectively. Again, there is a failure to distinguish differential concerns (and effects) of dry air as a source of stress. The contrasts between general concerns provided by the conceptualization of aviation psychology as a craft or scientific discipline, as opposed to an applied science discipline, are essentially the same as for the specific flight deck topics. General concerns, such as stress and error and selection and training, can be concerns either of (re)design practice, guideline derivation, or knowledge acquisition, but not only of craft practice or only of scientific knowledge acquisition.

Following this conceptualization of general concerns, consideration is given to novel concerns outside the topics of this volume, including the concept of the electronic crewmember; the provision of in-flight interactive terminals to passengers; and the proposed use of pilots, travelling as passengers, to help aircrew in cases of emergency. Each will be conceptualized in turn.

In terms of the flight deck, the electronic crewmember is to be conceptualized as an enhancement of the physical (speech synthesizer, etc.) and abstract (artificial intelligence algorithms, etc.) structures of the interactive flightsystem's devices. The enhancement would increase physical and abstract resource costs of the devices. It would also extend the behaviour(s) of the devices relative to those of the aircrew and so increase the devices' behavioural resource costs. The structural and behavioural resource costs of the aircrew might also change depending on how the aircrew's and the electronic crewmember's behaviour(s) were optimized. Flightsystem effectiveness might or might not be affected (either positively or negatively).

The provision of in-flight terminals to passengers for electronic (duty free) shopping, banking (ordering/changing currency), and communication (fax) is to be conceptualized in terms of a passenger attribute (satisfaction with in-flight facilities) that might be used to specify (satisfied, dissatisfied) in part the task quality of air passenger transportation. The provision of in-flight terminals is thus analogous to (but not identical with) the provision of meals. Were a commercial manager, however, to use the fax facility to conduct business, the provision of a terminal to the passenger would be like the enhancement of the flight deck devices by the addition of an electronic crewmember as conceptualized earlier. The terminal would then be conceptualized in terms of its structures, behaviours and resource costs, but as they relate to interactive office systems applied to the domain of business transactions, and not to interactive flightsystems as applied to the domain of air passenger transport.

Lastly, the use of pilots travelling as passengers to be used in the case of emergency (e.g. fire, pilot disablement) is to be conceptualized in the same way as an additional or substitute crewmember (as might occur following a stopover, for example). However, depending upon whether the relationship with the aircrew (and passengers) was that of passenger-pilot (for example, with one on every flight, with well-trained specialist skills in integrating with an aircrew in an emergency) or that of pilot-passenger (for example, simply happening to be on board and trained only in standard emergency skills), the conceptualization would be weighted toward that of a pilot or that of a passenger respectively.

In terms of aviation psychology, the novel concerns of electronic crewmember, provision of in-flight terminals, and use of pilots travelling as passengers in an emergency are to be conceptualized in terms of an applied discipline as (re)design practice, guideline derivation or knowledge acquisition. Given the novelty of the concerns they are, not surprisingly, the subject of knowledge acquisition rather than of design practice or guideline derivation. This completes the conceptualization of novel concerns not addressed by these volumes.

As with the conceptualization of the specific and general concerns, the relations exposed between the novel concerns differ from those presumed by alternative conceptualizations. For example, the novel concerns discussed above would all be most naturally conceptualized in terms of efficiency, rather than well-being. The electronic crewmember and emergency aiding would be assumed to enhance pilot efficiency, and in-flight terminals to support passenger efficiency (in ordering duty free goods, etc.). The difference between the work of air passenger transportation and the flightsystem for effecting the transport is less easily distinguished by this conceptualization. Alternatively, the flight deck conceptualized in terms of functionality, usability and acceptability would assume all the concerns to relate to functionality – the electronic crewmember and the in-flight terminals involving a change in the allocation of function between human and device, the emergency pilot-passenger (or passenger-pilot) a change in the allocation of function between aircrew members (in cases of emergency). In addition, the electronic crewmember and the in-flight terminals would be assumed to relate to usability and to acceptability. Although this approach and the one proposed here both conceptualize in-flight terminal acceptability, the former's conceptualization is with respect to the device, while the latter's is additionally related to the effectiveness of air passenger transportation.

Again, the conceptualization of aviation psychology as a craft or scientific discipline provides the same contrasts as for specific and general concerns as indicated earlier. This completes the application of the conceptualization to the flight deck and to aviation psychology.

CONCLUSION

This paper began by setting out the requirements for a conceptualization to relate specific, general, and novel concerns associated with aviation psychology on the flight deck. The conceptualization was intended to relate explicitly and coherently those topics that might otherwise be related only implicitly. To this end, the paper proposed an expression of the flight deck appropriate for the concerns of aviation psychology, and an expression of aviation psychology appropriate for the flight deck. The conceptualization was applied to the specific, general, and novel concerns of aviation psychology on the flight deck. These topics and concerns were explicitly and coherently related by a conceptualization of the interactive flightsystem, comprising aircrew and flight deck devices; the domains of transporting passengers by air; and the performance with which the system flies the aircraft; and a conceptualization of applied aviation psychology, comprising knowledge and practices seeking the solution to a general problem having the particular scope of designing the aircrew's interaction with the flight deck's devices to transport passengers effectively. Since the specific, general, and novel concerns were successfully conceptualized, the original requirements set out by the paper can be seen to have been met. In addition, the conceptualization exposed relations between topics and concerns not exposed by alternative conceptualizations (for example, in terms of efficiency and well-being; or in terms of functionality, usability and acceptability).

The conceptualization proposed is of, and so particular to, aviation psychology on the civil flight deck. Since it claims to be coherent and complete with respect to the concerns to which it has been applied, it offers a modest contribution to the development of a consensus view of aviation psychology on the flight deck. However, the conceptions from which the conceptualization was derived are general, and are not particular either to aviation psychology (as opposed to naval psychology, management psychology, nursing psychology – see Long & Dowell, 1989) or to the flight deck (as opposed to the factory floor, the office, the boardroom – see Dowell & Long, 1989). Being general, the conceptions make possible a general consensus view of work and worksystems with respect to disciplines intended for their support. However, a general consensus view can be developed only on the basis of particular conceptualizations. The present conceptualization of aviation psychology on the flight deck is, then, also offered as a contribution to the development of a general consensus view of work and worksystems with respect to disciplines intended for their support.

ACKNOWLEDGEMENT

This paper has benefited (as ever) from a critical review by John Dowell, colleague at the Ergonomics Unit, University College London. Any remaining infelicities are entirely my own.

REFERENCES

Long, J. and Dowell, J. (1989). Conceptions of the discipline of HCI: Craft, applied science, and engineering. In A. Sutcliffe and L Macaulay (Eds.),

People and Computers V. Cambridge: Cambridge University Press.

Dowell, J. and Long, J. (1989). Towards a conception for an engineering discipline of human factors. *Ergonomics,* 32, 1513-1535.

Index